American Language Hub

LEVEL 1B
Workbook

with Key + access to Audio

ADRIAN TENNANT

macmillan education

Macmillan Education Limited
4 Crinan Street
London N1 9XW

Companies and representatives throughout the world

American Language Hub Level 1B Workbook with Key
ISBN 978-1-380-04697-0
American Language Hub Level 1B Workbook with Key + access to Audio
ISBN 978-1-380-04691-8

Written by Adrian Tennant

First published 2020

Original design by emc design ltd
Page make-up by SPi Global
Cover design based on an original design by Restless
Cover photograph by Plainpicture/Cultura/dotdotred
Picture research by Emily Taylor

The authors and publishers would like to thank the following for permission to reproduce their photographs:

Alamy/Magone p46(1); **Digital Vision** p40(3); **Ehaurylik** p50(3); **Getty Images** pp40(2), 46(2,9), 48(cl), 52(1), 66(7, 11), 68, 74, Getty Images/Allsport Concepts Creative p66(4), Getty Images/Andrea Zanchi Photography p49, Getty Images/Petek Arici p42(4), Getty Images/Thomas Barwick pp43(1), 56, 68(1), Getty Images/Blend Images pp55, 66(3), 68(3), Getty Images/Alistair Berg p52(4), Getty Images/Nick Brundle p58(cl), Getty Images/Anna Bryukhanova p42(2), Getty Images/Caiaimage p61(bl), Getty Images/Petar Chernaev p42(3), Getty Images/Paolo Cipriani p42(5), Getty Images/Corbis p52(3), Getty Images/Cultura pp47, 50(2), 53(tl), 67, 69(br), 70, Getty Images/Robert Decelis p57, Getty Images/Digital Vision pp43(3), 52(2), 68(5,6), Getty Images/Dorling Kindersley p66(9), Getty Images/E+ pp52(a), 68(tr,tl), Getty Images/EyeEm pp46(4), 52(b,c,d), 58(tl), 61(tl), 62(1), 75, Getty Images/Hero Images p69(tcr), Getty Images/Imagemore p66(2), Getty Images/iStockphoto pp51, 74(b), Getty Images/Jeff Kauck Photography p48(tr), Getty Images/Roos Koole p69(bcr), Getty Images/Johner RF p68(4), Getty Images/Loop Images/Alan Novelli p54, Getty Images/Moment p64, Getty Images/National Geographic Creative p66(6), Getty Images/Thomas Northcut p53(bl), Getty Images/Pagadesign p74(c), Getty Images/Passage pp60(b), 65, Getty Images/PeopleImages p66(5), Getty Images/Photolibrary p46(3), Getty Images/Tanatat Pongpibool p59, Getty Images/Martin Poole p46(5), Getty Images/Andre Schoenherr p62(2), Getty Images/Alexander Spatari p41, Getty Images/Shannon Stent p66(8), Getty Images/The Image Bank pp43(2), 71, 72, Getty Images/Tbradford p45, Getty Images/Betsie Van der Meer p42(1), Getty Images/Sharon Vos-Arnold p40(1), Getty Images/Westend61, pp60(tl), 66(10,12), 73, Getty Images/Natalie Winter p58(bl), Getty Images/Yagi Studio p63, Getty Images/Bahadir Yeniceri p46(7); **Dave G Kelly** p66(1); **Macmillan Education Limited** p46(10); **Photodisc**/C Squared Studios p40(6); **Shutterstock**/Dokmaihaeng p50(1), Shutterstock/S-F p40(5); **Stockbyte**/John Foxx p40(4); **Thinkstock** p46(8); **Up the Resolution** p46(6).

Printed and bound in Uruguay

2023

2

Contents

7.1 Travel and Transportation

VOCABULARY
Transportation

A Match pictures (1–6) with the words in the box.

bicycle ferry plane taxi
trolley subway train

1 ______

2 ______

3 ______

4 ______

5 ______

6 ______

B Complete the types of transportation in sentences (1–6).

1 We took a small **b** _ _ _ to the island.
2 Tom always feels nervous before he flies on a **p** _ _ _ _.
3 My sister was five when she learned to ride a **b** _ _ _ _ _ _.
4 When we visited San Francisco last year, we traveled around the city by **t** _ _ _ _ _ _.
5 There's a **b** _ _ stop right outside my house!
6 Mike fell off his **m** _ _ _ _ _ _ _ _ _, but he was OK because he always wears a helmet.

PRONUNCIATION
/eɪ/ and /oʊ/

7.1 Complete the table with the words in the box. Then listen and check.

boat coach main motorcycle
phone plane same train

/eɪ/	/oʊ/

GRAMMAR
could

Look at pictures (1–6) and complete the sentences with *could* or *couldn't*.

1 Sophie ______ read before she started school.

2 Five years ago, Callum ______ swim.

3 I ______ speak Japanese when I first moved to Tokyo.

4 Fifty years ago, you ______ buy a car for under $1,000.

5 When she was young, Emily ______ run really fast.

6 I had trumpet lessons when I was ten, but ______ play very well.

7.2 Travel and Transportion

A love of adventure

VOCABULARY
Travel phrases

A Cross out the incorrect noun in each group.

1 We were late so we missed the *bus / travel / train*.
2 Ana returned *home / from New York / the flight* last week.
3 They were really excited when they arrived *the scooter / at the hotel / in Hong Kong*.
4 Susi and Dewi decided not to take *the hotel / the ferry / a taxi* as it was too expensive.
5 We left *the station / the motorcycle / for Seoul* 30 minutes late.

B Complete the review using phrases from Exercise A.

★☆☆☆☆ 1 day ago

American nightmare

Mark T

We [1] ________________ last night. Unfortunately, the whole vacation was terrible. The guidebook said it wasn't a good idea to [2] ________________ from the airport to the city center as traffic is bad and it's expensive.

When we finally [3] ________________ in Manhattan, the receptionist told us we couldn't check in for another four hours!

The next morning we [4] ________________ to go on the sightseeing tour, and so we had to go on our own. We wanted to see the Statue of Liberty. Unfortunately, we [5] ________________ 30 minutes late and missed the last ferry of the day. We were so unlucky!

GRAMMAR
Simple past negative

Rewrite the sentences in the simple past negative.

1 I watched the news this morning.
I didn't watch the news this morning.
2 Mae studied German at school.
____
3 I saw Simon and Alison at the party on Saturday.
____
4 I went to the gym after work.
____
5 I liked math when I was in school.
____
6 Lizzie finished the report yesterday.
____
7 I spoke to him after the meeting.
____
8 Molly enjoyed that movie last night.
____

PRONUNCIATION
Word stress: cities

7.2 Underline the stressed syllable in each city. Then listen and check.

1 Paris
2 Bangkok
3 Berlin
4 Caracas
5 Milan
6 Kathmandu
7 Lisbon
8 Manila
9 Mumbai
10 Chicago

GRAMMAR
Simple past questions

Complete the conversation with the simple past form of the verbs in parentheses. Add question words where necessary.

Karen: Hi Sabrina. 1 ___*Was*___ (*be*) it your birthday on Saturday?

Sabrina: Oh, hey Karen. Yes, it was.

Karen: 2 __________ (*go*) to a restaurant with your family?

Sabrina: No, I had a party.

Karen: Oh, really? I didn't get an invite on Facebook …

Sabrina: Oh, sorry. I thought you were on vacation last week.

Karen: I was, but I got back on Friday. Don't worry. So, 3 __________ (*have*) the party?

Sabrina: At my house. We sat in the yard because the weather was so good.

Karen: Oh, that sounds nice. So, 4 __________ (*eat*)?

Sabrina: We had a barbecue and my sister-in-law brought some of that nice ice cream from that store near the movie theater.

Karen: Oh, wow! That stuff is delicious. So … 5 __________ (*be*) Tom at the party?

Sabrina: No, he wasn't. He had to work all weekend.

Karen: 6 __________ (*take*) any photos?

Sabrina: Of course. Do you want to see them?

Karen: Sure. Wow! It's really dark. 7 __________ (*do*) the party end?

Sabrina: Uh … about midnight I think. My dad was worried about complaints from the neighbors.

PRONUNCIATION
Connected speech

7.3 **Listen to the questions and sentences. Draw a ‿ between words that are linked together.**

1 What did you do on the weekend?
2 How long did you work there?
3 They stayed there for two weeks.
4 Susan didn't want to go home.
5 Did you have fun?
6 Where did you go last summer?
7 Did you stay in a hotel?
8 We went to a lot of museums.

VOCABULARY
Verb phrases

Look at the pictures. Complete the sentences with an appropriate simple past verb.

1 I __________ shopping with Emily on Saturday.

2 Tim __________ lost and had to ask directions.

3 I __________ a lot of interesting people at the party on Saturday.

4 Ji Yeon and I __________ some great food at the street market on Sunday.

5 Bea __________ a lot of photos on vacation in Italy last summer.

Three **amazing** ways to work in **another country**

Want to live in another country for a few months, but don't have the cash? Here's how to start your adventure.

a 'WWOOFING'

Lots of farms around the world are part of a project that lets people learn about life on a farm for free. If you like animals and the countryside, then you will love it – just be prepared to wake up at 6 am and work outside in all kinds of weather! Many people make very close friends with the other workers as the [1]**destination** usually isn't near a city, meaning you spend all of your free time together. Another important [2]**detail** is that you will only be paid for your hard work through free meals and somewhere to sleep; if you want to save money, this isn't for you.

b Tour Guide

Do you know a lot about a place in another country? Perhaps you could find a job as a tour guide taking other visitors around and showing them all the [3]**sights**. You need to know about the history of the place and be able to remember lots of information. You can also learn a lot from the other tour guides, as sometimes they know lots of [4]**fascinating** facts. You will get paid for your work and you can also make extra from the [5]**tips** that people give you at the end of each tour.

c Working in a hostel

Hostels are [6]**budget** hotels where people can stay when they visit a new place. When people stay in a hostel they sometimes [7]**share** a bedroom and showers. There are lots of different jobs in a hostel that are similar to the ones in a hotel. You can find work as a receptionist or helping to clean the rooms. It is often possible to find work in a hostel, especially during the [8]**peak season** when the hostels can be full of people. When you work you will be paid, but some of your money will go toward paying for your room and meals.

READING

A READ FOR GIST Read *Three amazing ways to work in another country*. Match pictures (1–3) to jobs (a–c).

B IDENTIFY MEANING FROM CONTEXT Read again. Choose the correct meaning of the words in bold.

1. **a** the place you're going
   b a place where you stay
2. **a** everything you need to know about something
   b one small piece of information
3. **a** places you can buy things
   b interesting places that people go to see
4. **a** very interesting
   b fairly surprising
5. **a** extra money someone gives you
   b extra information about something
6. **a** not very expensive
   b very expensive
7. **a** to want something that belongs to someone else
   b to use something at the same time as another person
8. **a** the time of year when many people visit a place
   b a time of year when a place isn't very busy

C READ FOR DETAIL Read the article again. Choose the correct jobs to complete the sentences.

1. You don't get paid any money working as a *farm worker / tour guide / hostel worker*.
2. There are different jobs you can do as a *farm worker / tour guide / hostel worker*.
3. You need to know facts about the place to work as a *farm worker / tour guide / hostel worker*.
4. When you work as a *farm worker / tour guide / hostel worker* you spend a lot of time talking to people.
5. You won't get all of your money when you work as a *farm worker / tour guide / hostel worker* and stay there as well.
6. When you work as a *farm worker / tour guide / hostel worker* you start very early in the morning.
7. Working as *farm worker / tour guide / hostel worker* you don't usually work in a city.

D REFLECT Would you like to go on a working vacation? Why/Why not?

LISTENING

7.4 **A LISTEN FOR GIST** Listen to an interview about a journey around the world. Mark the route on the map.

7.4 **B LISTEN FOR DETAIL** Listen again. Are these sentences true (T) or false (F)? Correct the false sentences.

1. Tom didn't want to travel anywhere by plane. *T/F*
2. He traveled from Paris to Athens by train. *T/F*
3. He bought a motorcycle in Nairobi. *T/F*
4. It took three weeks to get from Singapore to the US. *T/F*
5. Tom says he met some very unusual people. *T/F*
6. He says it was strange to stay in hotels in the US because they were so normal. *T/F*

C REFLECT Answer the questions.

1. What do you think of Tom's journey?
2. Would you like to go on a similar journey? Why/ Why not?
3. What do you think would be the most interesting part of the journey? Why?

FUNCTIONAL LANGUAGE

Checking in and out of a hotel

7.5 Complete the conversation with the words in the box. Then listen and check.

afternoon checkout help included passport password reservation wi-fi

Receptionist: Good [1] ________, sir. How can I help you?

Tom: I have a [2] ________ for a double room for two nights.

Receptionist: OK, great. Could I have your [3] ________, please?

Tom: Of course. Here you are. What time is [4] ________ on Sunday?

Receptionist: It's at noon, sir.

Tom: Great, and is breakfast [5] ________?

Receptionist: Yes, it is. It's between 6:30 and 10 am in the dining room. Do you need any [6] ________ with your bags?

Tom: No, I'm fine thank you. Is there [7] ________ in the rooms?

Receptionist: Yes, there is. The [8] ________ is on the desk in your room.

Tom: OK, great. Thank you.

Receptionist: You're welcome, sir. Do you need anything else?

Tom: Uh … yes. Can I have my key?

TRAVEL SPOTLIGHT: SIEM REAP

Last December I went to Siem Reap in Cambodia with my husband. [1]___, so it seemed like the perfect choice.

Siem Reap is a fairly big town with lots of places to eat and stay. Of course, there are expensive hotels, but we couldn't afford one of those. [2]___

There are lots of activities and interesting places to see and visit, so you won't be bored! [3]___ It was a great way to sightsee in a short time. We also both enjoy shopping and there were lots of stores to buy souvenirs. So every day was completely different!

For me it was a great vacation because I did all the things I enjoy and the weather was sunny but not too hot. [4]___ There were a lot more tourists than I thought there would be.

WRITING

A **Read *Travel spotlight: Siem Reap*. Complete blanks (1–4) by choosing sentences (a–e). There is one extra sentence that you do not need.**

- **a** We chose a small family-run place and met some really friendly people.
- **b** We went to a different restaurant every evening and we ate some really nice food.
- **c** We are both really interested in history and it is close to the famous temples of Angkor Wat.
- **d** Probably the only thing that we didn't like was that the temples were crowded.
- **e** On one of the days, we went on a bike tour around the city.

B **Read the article again. Complete the sentences with no more than two words from the text.**

1. The writer went to Siem Reap in ________.
2. She couldn't afford to stay in an ________.
3. While she was there, she did some sightseeing and shopped for ________.
4. She describes the weather as sunny, but not ________.
5. She didn't enjoy the temples because there were a lot of ________ there.

C **Complete the sentences with *so* and *because*.**

1. We went in February ________ it isn't as hot as other times of the year.
2. There were lots of cheap stores ________ we bought lots of souvenirs.
3. We don't usually go on long flights ________ we are both frightened of flying.
4. I didn't really enjoy the museums ________ they were full of tourists.
5. We didn't have time to see everything, ________ we both want to go back there again.

WRITING PRACTICE

A **PLAN You are going to write about a travel experience. Write notes about:**

- where you went
- where you stayed
- what you did there
- what the weather was like
- what you liked/didn't like

B **WRITE Use your notes to write a short article/blog entry. Use *so* and *because* to join your ideas.**

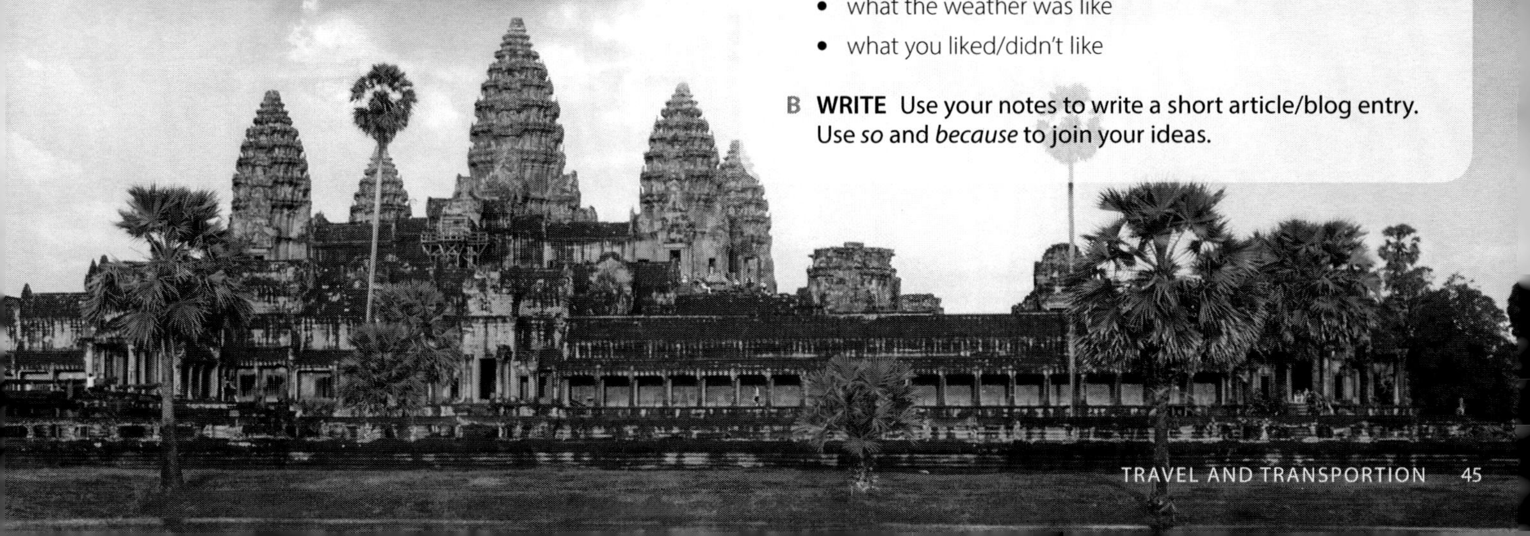

8.1 Food and Drink

I'm hungry!

VOCABULARY
Food and drink

A Look at the pictures and complete the crossword.

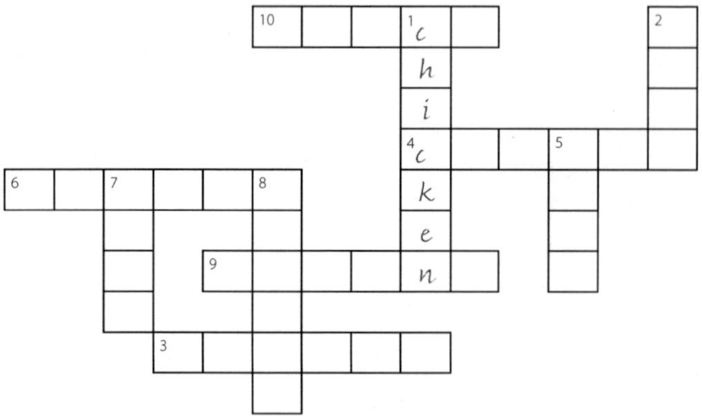

DOWN

1 

2 

5 

7 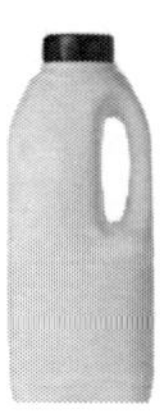

8 

ACROSS

3 

4 

6 

9 

10 

GRAMMAR
Countable and uncountable nouns; *some* and *any*

A Find and correct eleven mistakes in the blog post below.

Health goals

JENNA THOMPSON | October 23, 2018 | 97 COMMENTS

This week, I'm trying to be healthier. So instead of snacks like a bar of chocolate, I'll eat any fruit, like a apple, a banana or some oranges. I never eat breakfast, but this morning I had a bowl of cereal with milks and a toast without some butter.

At lunchtime, I went to a café close to where I work. I ordered some brown rices with chicken and a glass of juices. Then for dessert I had some yogurt.

In the evening, I usually have some sandwiches, but this evening I'm going to have some fishes with a vegetables and any cheeses and biscuits.

B Complete the table with the words in the box.

apple banana cookie chips hamburgers mushroom pasta potatoes rice sandwiches toast yogurt

Countable singular	Countable plural	Uncountable

PRONUNCIATION
Plurals

8.1 Listen and circle the word with a different plural ending sound in each group.

1	potatoes	hamburgers	chips
2	oranges	sausages	tomatoes
3	carrots	peas	nuts

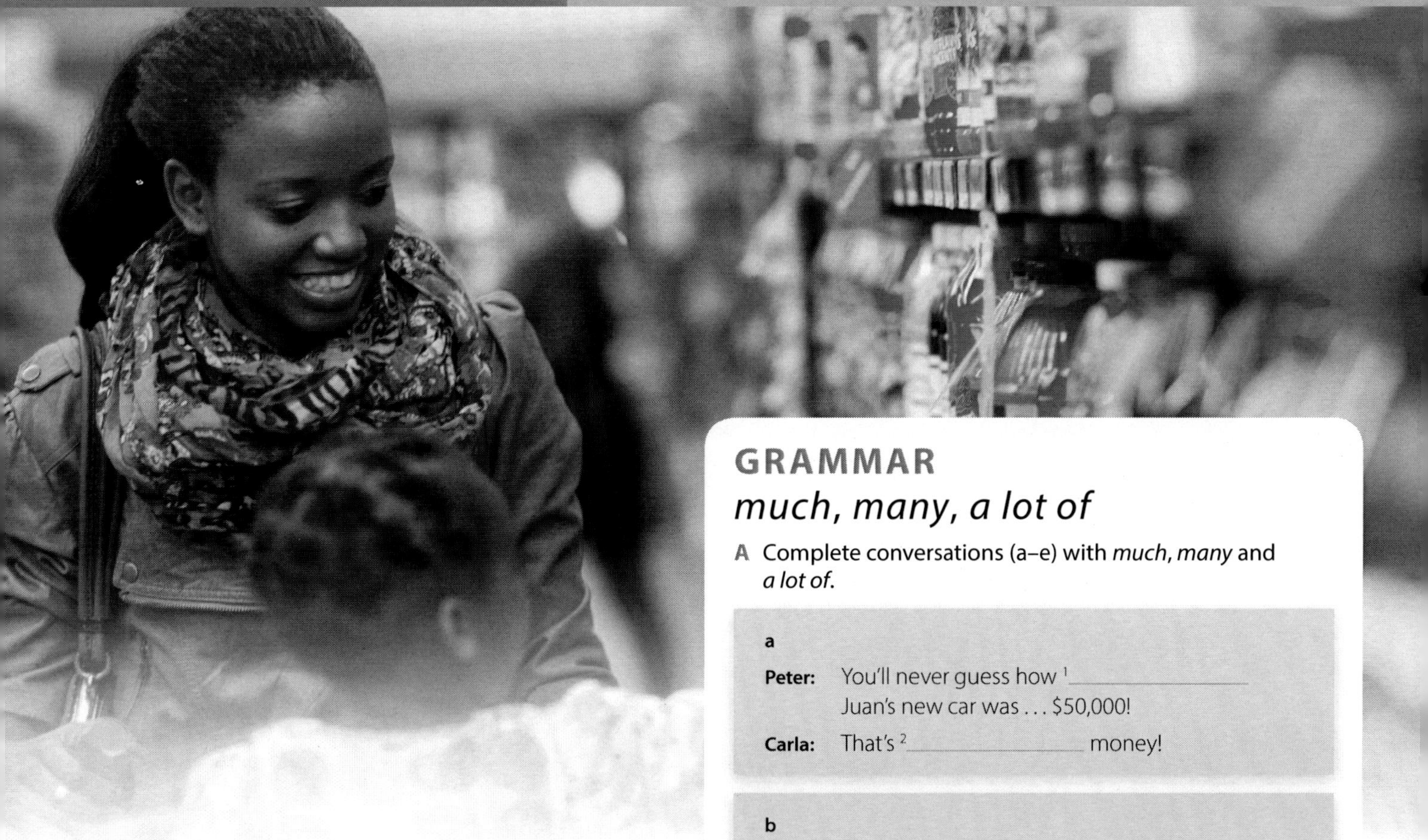

GRAMMAR
much, many, a lot of

A Complete conversations (a–e) with *much*, *many* and *a lot of*.

a

Peter: You'll never guess how [1]__________ Juan's new car was . . . $50,000!

Carla: That's [2]__________ money!

b

James: How [3]__________ people are coming to our barbecue tonight?

Tom: About 35. So we'll need [4]__________ food.

c

Jacob: How [5]__________ pasta do we have?

Rick: Uh, there's [6]__________ rice, but no pasta.

d

Alex: Our teacher gave us [7]__________ homework to do tonight.

Sam: That's OK because there aren't [8]__________ days left before our test.

e

Toni: How [9]__________ sugar do you take in your tea?

Eleanor: I don't take very [10]__________, just half a teaspoon.

B Are these sentences correct or incorrect? Correct the incorrect ones.

1 How many bread do you usually eat?
2 We have a lot of eggs in the fridge.
3 Karen drinks much coffee in the morning.
4 How much milk do you have in your coffee?
5 There aren't much bananas left. Can you buy some?
6 How much people did you invite to the party?

VOCABULARY
Containers

Cross out the incorrect noun in each sentence.

1 Can you go and get a can of ***beans*** / ***soup*** / ***rice*** for me?
2 Can you buy a big carton of ***milk*** / ***sparkling water*** / ***apple juice*** at the store?
3 I'd like two packages of ***chocolate cookies*** / ***chips*** / ***yogurt*** please.
4 We need one more jar of ***chocolates*** / ***coffee*** / ***sauce***.
5 Can you buy a box of ***chocolates*** / ***sauce*** / ***cereal*** on your way home?
6 We also need to get a bottle of ***yogurt*** / ***orange juice*** / ***milk*** for your grandmother.

PRONUNCIATION
Short and long vowel sounds

8.2 Listen and write the words you hear in the correct circle.

SHORT VOWEL SOUNDS

LONG VOWEL SOUNDS

GRAMMAR
a/an, *the*, no article

A Choose the correct options to complete the rules.

1. We use ***a* or *an* / *the*** when we talk about a singular noun for the first time.
2. We use ***a* or *an* / *the*** with plural nouns when it is clear what we are talking about.
3. We use ***the* / *no article*** when we talk about things in general.
4. We use ***the* / *no article*** with singular nouns when there is only one.
5. We use ***a* or *an* / *no article*** with the names of people and things, cities and most countries.

B Complete the text with *a/an*, *the* or no article.

Bradley Cooper
American actor, director and producer

Bradley Cooper was born in [1]_____ Philadelphia in 1975. He is [2]_____ actor who has been in [3]_____ movies such as *Silver Linings Playbook* and is also [4]_____ voice of [5]_____ Rocket Raccoon in *Guardians of the Galaxy*. He is famous all over [6]_____ world, but one thing you might not know about him is that he is [7]_____ excellent cook. He said in [8]_____ interview that he learned many skills from playing [9]_____ chef in [10]_____ TV show *Kitchen Confidential* and [11]_____ movie *Burnt*. [12]_____ TV show was based on [13]_____ book by Anthony Bourdain, who was also from [14]_____ US.

PRONUNCIATION
Consonant clusters

8.3 **Listen and underline the consonant clusters in these words.**

1. flour
2. fruit
3. healthy
4. bottle
5. vegetables
6. fry
7. bowl
8. sandwich

VOCABULARY
Food preparation

A Choose the correct verbs to complete the recipe.

Easy pancakes recipe

INGREDIENTS

100 g flour
300 ml milk
2 large eggs
1 tbsp oil
Pinch of salt
Sugar/lemon for serving

METHOD

1. ***Peel / Put / Serve*** the flour, milk and some salt into a bowl.
2. ***Chop / Crack / Fry*** two eggs into the mixture.
3. ***Beat / Fry / Put*** the mixture together and leave for 30 minutes.
4. ***Add / Crack / Heat*** some oil in a frying pan.
5. Put some of the mixture into the pan and ***beat / fry / heat*** on each side for one minute.
6. ***Chop / Put / Serve*** with some sugar, lemon juice or maple syrup.

B Complete the sentences with the words in the box.

add	chop	fry	grate	peel	put	serve

1. Can you ________ a banana, for me?
2. Why don't you ________ some cheese on the top before you put it in the oven?
3. ________ all the eggs in the bowl.
4. When it's ready to eat, ________ it with some bread.
5. Put some oil in the pan and ________ the mushrooms for about four minutes.
6. To make the sauce, ________ some tomatoes into small pieces.
7. ________ some salt and pepper to make everything taste nice.

Trying something new

JENNY MACKINTOSH | November 12, 2018 | 658 COMMENTS

I love food, and when I go on vacation, I try to eat local food that is **unique** to the area. Of course, I always look for the healthy options, but I also try to find 'strange' food. I know that for the people that live there the food probably isn't strange, but it's not the type of food I'm used to.

Last year in Cambodia I was traveling down a road and saw a man serving food from a stand. I stopped and looked; he was cooking **frogs**! I know they eat these in some countries, but it was my first time – they were delicious and **tasted** a little like chicken! Later on, I went to a restaurant where everything was made from insects. I can't say that everything was nice and, in fact, some of it was terrible, but I tried it.

In Japan I ate some fish that was **poisonous**, and I had a soup in China that was made with poisonous mushrooms, too. Both dishes were delicious, but I don't think I would eat them again as I was nervous the whole time!

The funny thing is I'm from Scotland and we eat some strange food there. I'm not talking about the food we fry, but one dish in particular – Haggis. This is made from the **stomach** of a sheep and we often eat it with *tatties*, a name we give to potatoes, and *neeps*, which are a kind of vegetable. I love it!

READING

A READ FOR GIST Read *Trying something new*. Choose the best title.

1 Great food
2 Unusual food
3 Terrible food

B READ FOR DETAIL Read the blog post again. Choose the correct options (a, b or c) to complete the sentences.

1 When Jenny is on vacation she tries to find and eat food that …
   a she likes.
   b is unhealthy.
   c she doesn't usually eat.
2 When Jenny ate frogs she thought they …
   a tasted delicious.
   b were chicken.
   c were not from Cambodia.
3 She went to a restaurant where you could only eat …
   a local food.
   b food where insects were one of the ingredients.
   c soups.
4 In Japan and China she ate dishes …
   a made from fish.
   b made from mushrooms.
   c that were delicious.
5 One of her favorite dishes is …
   a fried.
   b Haggis.
   c a type of vegetable.

C SCAN Scan the post again. What part of speech (noun, adjective or verb) are the words in bold?

1 unique ....
2 frog ....
3 taste ....
4 poisonous ....
5 stomach ....

D DECODE Read again. Match definitions (a–e) with the words in Exercise C (1–5).

a to have a particular flavor
b the part of your body where food goes after it's eaten
c like no other
d a small animal with long back legs that lives in water
e causing death or illness if eaten

E REFLECT Would you eat any of the food described in the blog?

LISTENING

8.4 **A LISTEN FOR GIST** Listen to a conversation about food. Who likes the food in pictures (1–3) – Oli or Tara?

8.4 **B LISTEN FOR DETAIL** Listen again and answer the questions.

1 What does Tara say about hot dogs and burgers?
   a She eats them all the time.
   b They are very healthy.
   c She thinks they are delicious.

2 What does Oli think about hot dogs and burgers?
   a They are delicious.
   b They are unhealthy.
   c They are healthy.

3 What does Tara usually eat?
   a hot dogs
   b salads
   c Thai food

4 What does Oli say about his favorite Thai dish?
   a It's hot and spicy.
   b It's made with coconut milk.
   c It's delicious with rice.

5 What type of food do Oli and Tara go to eat?
   a Italian
   b American
   c Thai

6 How does Tara describe the slices at the pizza place?
   a delicious
   b great
   c enormous

C REFLECT Are you more like Oli or Tara? Why?

FUNCTIONAL LANGUAGE
Ordering food in a restaurant

A **Match the beginnings of the sentences (1–6) with the ends of the sentences (a–f).**

1 Are you ready …	a mango juice with ice?
2 Yes, I'll have …	b to drink?
3 OK. Would you like something …	c the dessert menu?
4 Could I have a …	d the chicken salad, please.
5 Would you like to see …	e bill, please?
6 No, thanks. Can I have the …	f to order?

8.5 **B** Listen and check your answers to Exercise A.

Glossary
spicy (adj) spicy food has a hot flavor

★★★★★ 2 days ago
Meow
Haruto

I love cake and cats, so I was very happy when I found this café that has both of [1]**them!** Basically, you can order something to eat and hold or play with a cat at the same time. One of the cats was so nice I wanted to take [2]**him** home. My waitress was very helpful and [3]**she** told me to order the chocolate cake and tea with milk – [4]**they** were both amazing! [5]**It**'s very popular so go before lunchtime.

★★★☆☆ 3 days ago
At Night
Ralph S

At Night is a special restaurant where everything is dark! My girlfriend and I couldn't read the menu, but our waiter told us what was on [1]<u>the menu</u>. I ordered pasta. [2]<u>The pasta</u> was not easy to eat with no light. [3]<u>The pasta</u> was delicious though. My girlfriend ordered a mushroom dish and a vegetable side dish as [4]<u>my girlfriend</u> doesn't eat meat. Unfortunately, [5]<u>the mushroom dish and the vegetable side dish</u> were cold, so my girlfriend wanted to ask the waiter to take [6]<u>the mushroom dish and the vegetable side dish</u> back to the kitchen. The only problem was [7]<u>my girlfriend</u> couldn't see [8]<u>the waiter</u>!

WRITING

A Read the review of a cat café. What do the pronouns in bold refer to?

1 *cake and cats*
2 ______
3 ______
4 ______
5 ______

B Read the review of an unusual restaurant. Replace the <u>underlined</u> nouns with a suitable pronoun.

1 ______ 5 ______
2 ______ 6 ______
3 ______ 7 ______
4 ______ 8 ______

C Read the second review again and answer these questions.

1 Who did Ralph go to the restaurant with?
2 Why couldn't they read the menu?
3 What did the writer order?
4 What was his food like?
5 Why didn't his girlfriend enjoy her meal?

WRITING PRACTICE

A PREPARE You are going to write a review about an usual restaurant or café. Write notes about:

- the name of the restaurant or café
- who you went with
- the food you ate
- what was unusual about the restaurant
- the waiter / waitress

B WRITE Use your notes to write a review. Remember to use pronouns in your writing.

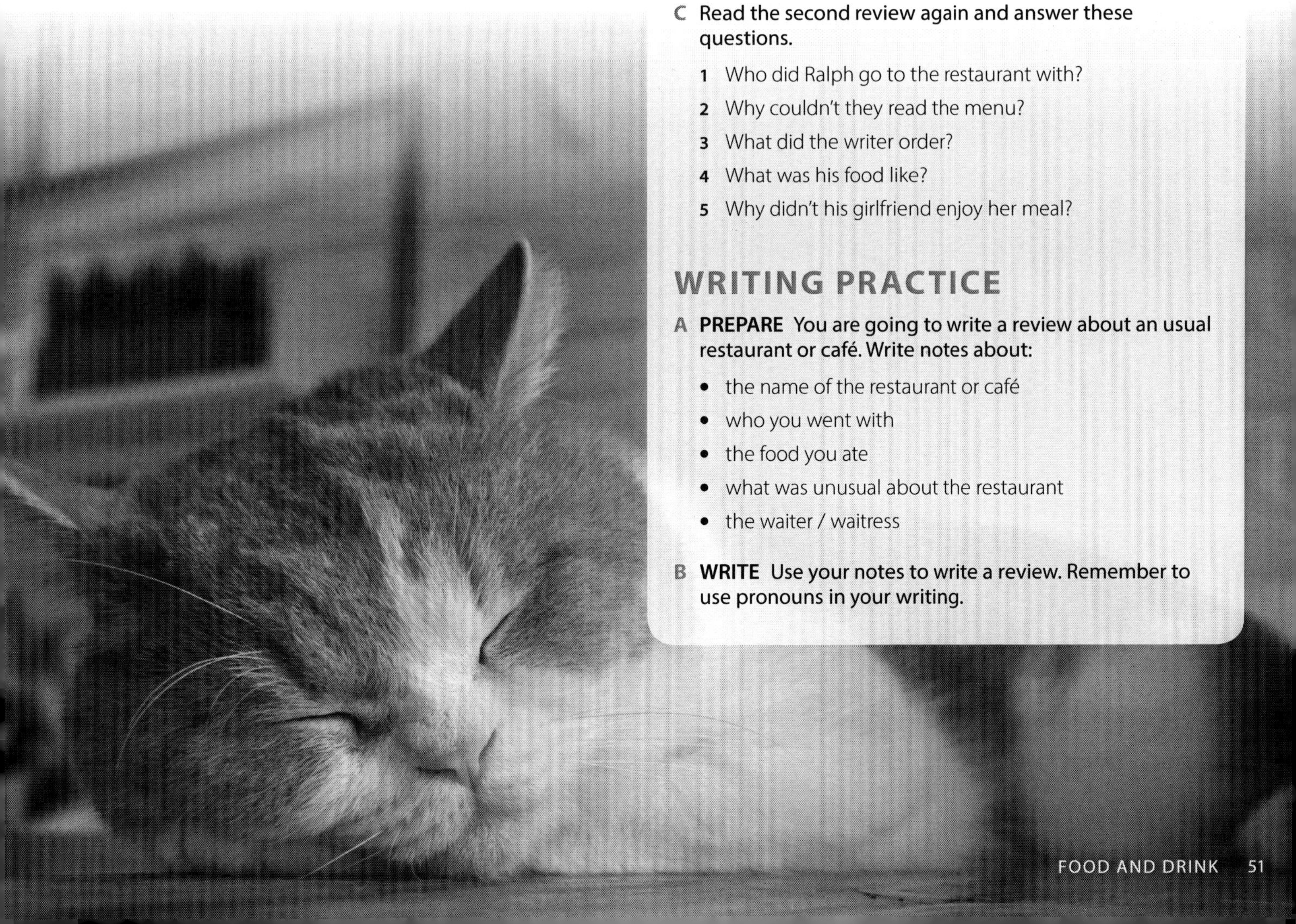

VOCABULARY
Clothes

Match the words in the box to pictures (1–4).

boots (x2) cap coat jacket (x2) jeans (x3)
scarf skirt sneakers socks sunglasses sweater

1

2

3

4

PRONUNCIATION
/ɜːr/

9.1 Underline the /ɜːr/ sound in these words. Then listen and check.

1 skirt
2 prefer
3 nurse
4 earn
5 work
6 girl
7 person
8 learn

GRAMMAR
Present progressive

A Complete the conversation with the present progressive form of the verb in parentheses. Use contractions where possible.

Anna: Hi Sally, what [1] *are you doing* (*you / do*)?
Sally: Right now I [2] ________ (*look*) at a dress.
Anna: Oh, so [3] ________ (*you / shop*).
Sally: Yes, [4] ________ (*Sara / help*) me find something for my interview tomorrow.
Anna: [5] ________ still ________ (*we / have*) lunch?
Sally: Yes, we are, don't worry! [6] ________ (*leave*) soon.
Anna: [7] ________ (*Ben / come*) too or [8] ________ (*work*) today?
Sally: No, [9] ________ (*work*). We'll see you in an hour.

B Use the prompts to write present progressive questions.

1 he / ride / a bike
2 he / eat / pizza
3 she / play / piano
4 they / run / in the park

C Look at images (1–4) and write short answers to the questions in Exercise B.

1 ________

2 ________

3 ________

4 ________

9.2 Shopping

VOCABULARY
Present time expressions

A Complete the texts with the time expressions in the boxes.

at the moment   these days   today

1 ______________, I'm studying a lot as I have exams next week. But 2 ______________, I'm relaxing at the beach. I'll study when I go home later 3 ______________.

currently   now   right now

Luca, come downstairs 4 ______________! We need to clean up the apartment. David called me saying he picked up Grandma just 5 ______________ and they are 6 ______________ driving over here.

B Choose the correct options to complete the sentences.

1. I'm *currently* / *today* in a meeting and unable to take your call.
2. I would like that report *right now* / *these days*!
3. I'm wearing a coat *these day* / *today* because it's cold.
4. I'm going swimming *now* / *at the moment* because it 's hot.
5. I love reading, but *these days* / *today*, I spend more time doing yoga.
6. *At the moment* / *Now*, I'm feeling really fit and healthy.

GRAMMAR
Simple present vs present progressive

A Complete the sentences with the simple present or present progressive form of the verbs in parentheses.

1. I sometimes ______________ (*work*) in a local charity store.
2. She ______________ (*not help*) out at her daughter's school today.
3. What ______________ (*they / watch*) right now?
4. They ______________ (*ride*) their bikes everywhere.
5. Rob usually ______________ (*walk*) to work.
6. Why ______________ (*you / leave*) now? It's too early.
7. This week we ______________ (*not close*) the store until 7:00 pm every night.

B Are the following sentences correct or incorrect? Correct the incorrect ones.

1. You should wear a scarf – it snows outside.
   ____
2. We aren't usually playing tennis every day.
   ____
3. Jamie is calling Rachel right now.
   ____
4. Are you usually going to the beach?
   ____
5. Max is writing an email at the moment.
   ____
6. She isn't currently cook in the kitchen.
   ____
7. Are they walk to school?
   ____

PRONUNCIATION
/ŋ/

9.2 **Listen and circle the words that have the /ŋ/ sound.**

1 sung
2 walking
3 sunglasses
4 pink
5 younger
6 sandwich
7 jeans
8 strong

GRAMMAR
Object pronouns

A Complete the table.

Subject pronoun	Object pronoun
I	me
he	
she	
it	
we	
you	
they	

B **Replace the underlined words with the correct object pronoun.**

1 I'm going for a walk with my cousin. Do you want to come with <u>my cousin and me</u>?
2 The phone is really cheap. Why don't you just buy <u>the phone</u>?
3 Are those jeans new? How much did you pay for <u>those jeans</u>?
4 There's a new Marvel movie at the movie theater. Have you seen <u>the new Marvel movie</u>?
5 That's a nice shirt. Your father would like it. Why don't you buy it for <u>your father</u>?
6 Stephanie is my best friend. Would you like to meet <u>Stephanie</u>?
7 What time are you and Maria leaving? I might leave with <u>you and Maria</u>.

VOCABULARY
Stores and services

A Complete the definitions with the words in the box.

bank dentist's department store hairdresser's pharmacy

1 ______________ a place where you get your teeth checked
2 ______________ a place where you can buy medicine
3 ______________ a place where you keep your money
4 ______________ a large store divided into lots of different parts
5 ______________ a place where you can get your hair cut

B Complete the paragraph with the words in the box.

bakery bookstore butcher's department store library market newsstand ~~supermarket~~

I grew up in a village. It didn't have a [1] *supermarket* so we went to the [2] ______________ to buy fresh bread, then to the [3] ______________ to get some meat. At the local [4] ______________, there were stands selling fruits and vegetables. There wasn't a [5] ______________, but we could borrow books from the local [6] ______________ for free. My dad always bought his paper from the [7] ______________. For clothes and things for the house, we went to the big [8] ______________ in the nearest town, which was 30 kilometers away.

PRONUNCIATION
/ʧ/ and /ʃ/

9.3 **Are the underlined sounds /ʧ/ or /ʃ/? Listen and choose the correct sounds.**

1 <u>ch</u>eese /ʃ/ /ʧ/
2 <u>sh</u>oes /ʃ/ /ʧ/
3 fa<u>sh</u>ion /ʃ/ /ʧ/
4 que<u>st</u>ion /ʃ/ /ʧ/
5 <u>s</u>ure /ʃ/ /ʧ/
6 sta<u>ti</u>on /ʃ/ /ʧ/
7 na<u>tu</u>re /ʃ/ /ʧ/
8 wa<u>sh</u> /ʃ/ /ʧ/

The 'perfect job'?
September 15

What a day! When I applied for the 'perfect job', I expected it to be easy. Yes, I'm enjoying it, but it's hard work. I usually wake up at around 6:00 am and go for a walk along the beach; it sounds nice, but actually at that time of the morning it can be fairly cold, and when it's raining it's not much fun. These days the weather is nice, but a month ago it was **terrible** every day. Today, I walked all the way to the far end of the island – that's about five kilometers, so it's a fairly long way. Currently, I'm writing my diary entry for the day, **uploading** some photos and checking my emails.

Tired of walking
September 16

5:30 am, Wow! Right now I'm sitting down and eating my breakfast. Last night I couldn't really sleep because it was very windy. Today, I have to walk around the island and check all the buildings to see what **damage** there is. When I first arrived here I thought it would be great living somewhere with no motorcycles or cars, but today I would love to be able to get on a motorcycle and not have to walk everywhere. It's days like today when I don't want to do this job anymore …

Hard work
September 19

I know I'm supposed to write my diary entry every day, but sometimes there isn't enough time. The last few days were **crazy**. When I got back to my room I was too tired to do anything apart from take off my clothes and fall into bed. At the moment I'm **organizing** things for today and tomorrow before I go outside to start work. I'm feeling **under pressure** at the moment, but I'm sure everything will be fine in the end.

READING

A READ FOR GENRE Read the blog posts and answer the questions.

1 Where is it from?
   a A magazine article
   b An online blog
2 Who is he writing for?
   a People interested in his job
   b People looking for a new job

Glossary

be supposed to (adj) used to show that you don't believe something that many others do
expected (adj) likely to happen or be true

B READ FOR SPECIFIC INFORMATION Read the blog posts again. Complete the sentences with no more than three words from the blog posts.

1 Joe thought the job would ________ when he applied for it.
2 After waking up in the morning he usually goes ________.
3 He doesn't think it's ________ when the weather is bad.
4 Because of the wind he couldn't ________.
5 He doesn't like having ________ because he doesn't have any transportation.
6 There isn't always ________ to write a diary entry.
7 He thinks that ________ everything will be fine.

C DECODE Scan the posts again. Complete definitions (1–6) with the words in bold.

1 ________ physical harm to something so it is broken and needs repairing
2 ________ preparing or arrange an activity or event
3 ________ sending documents or photos from your computer to the internet
4 ________ not sensible or practical
5 ________ feeling stressed because you have too much to do
6 ________ very bad

D REFLECT Answer the questions.

1 Do you think the job sounds like fun? Why/Why not?
2 What type of job do you think it is?
3 Do you know any unusual jobs?

LISTENING

A LISTEN FOR GIST Listen to five short radio advertisements for different stores. Match ads (1–5) with words (a–e). 9.4

a designer brands [1]
b discounts [ ]
c expensive [ ]
d high quality [ ]
e local [ ]

Glossary

in stock (phrase) when something is 'in stock', it is available in the store to buy immediately

B LISTEN FOR DETAIL Listen again. Are these sentences true (T) or false (F)? Correct the false sentences. 9.4

1. Max Out isn't open at the moment. T/F
2. Max Out doesn't have any bargains. T/F
3. JCs sells different products every week. T/F
4. Products at Bargains 2day are low quality. T/F
5. Clothes at Tuffin are expensive, but good quality. T/F
6. You can only buy ties at TieUp. T/F

C REFLECT Answer the questions.

1. Where do you usually buy your clothes?
2. Do you look for bargains and discounts?
3. Which of the five stores would you like to visit? Why?

FUNCTIONAL LANGUAGE
Shopping for clothes

Complete the conversation with the phrases in the box. Then listen and check. 9.5

a little small | Can I help you? | can I try | How much are they? | in medium | I'll take them | I'm just looking | look really great | the changing rooms

Store clerk: Good morning. [1] ________?
Customer: No, [2] ________, thank you.
Oh! Actually, [3] ________ these jeans on, please?
Store clerk: Of course, [4] ________ are over there.
Store clerk: Oh! They [5] ________ on you …
Customer: Thank you, but I think they are [6] ________. Do you have the same style [7] ________?
Store clerk: Yeah, here you are.
Customer: These are perfect. [8] ________?
Store clerk: They're $35, but there's a 10% discount.
Customer: Oh, great! [9] ________.

9.6 Shopping

Write a social media post

1. **Hannah**
1 hr ago

It's Sunday morning and we're go for our usual walk through the woods. I love picking wild mushrooms. You have to be careful as some are in danger, but there are lots that are delicious. Rick is trying to climb a tree … he's crazy!

2. **Mae**
45 mins ago

Hi, I'm down at the sports center with my friends rock climbing. We're having a grate time and trying to see how high we can get. It's my first time doing it and it's amazing! I' am happy we're inside. As we don't have to worry about the weather.

3. **Luke**
33 mins ago

We're traveling down to London to watch a play? We're taking the train as it's more relaxing. Jenny is playing a game on her tablet and Simon is listening to music. mom packed some sandwiches for us. so we're all eating those. More later.

WRITING

A Read the three social media posts. Which one matches the picture?

B Read the three posts again. Choose the correct names to complete the sentences.

1 *Hannah* / *Mae* / *Luke* is doing something for the first time.
2 *Hannah* / *Mae* / *Luke* is doing something they usually do.
3 *Hannah* / *Mae* / *Luke* is going somewhere to do something later.
4 *Hannah* / *Mae* / *Luke* writes about finding food.
5 *Hannah* / *Mae* / *Luke* is eating something at the moment.
6 *Hannah* / *Mae* / *Luke* is doing something that is done outside.

C Read the posts again. Find and correct eight mistakes.

WRITING PRACTICE

A **PREPARE** You are going to write a social media post. Write notes about:

- a picture you would use
- where you are
- who you are with
- what you are doing
- how you are feeling

B **WRITE** Use your notes to write your post.

C **REVIEW** Check your work for mistakes.

10.1 The Great Outdoors

VOCABULARY
Landscape features

Look at the pictures and complete the descriptions with the words in the box. Change the form if necessary.

beach desert forest hill island jungle lake mountain ocean river

This is a picture of Bled in Slovenia. It is famous for its beautiful [1] ______ with an [2] ______ in the center. Around the town you can see a [3] ______ and some snowy [4] ______.

Malaysia has many white sand [5] ______. This one is special though. The [6] ______ is so clear and in the background you can see [7] ______ covered in [8] ______, where you can go hiking if you're feeling adventurous!

This is one of my favorite places in Egypt. I love sailing down the [9] ______ with the empty [10] ______ all around us.

GRAMMAR
Comparatives

A Write the comparative form of these adjectives.

1 big *bigger*
2 old ______
3 easy ______
4 famous ______
5 good ______
6 cheap ______
7 close ______
8 expensive ______
9 dirty ______
10 bad ______
11 comfortable ______
12 strange ______

B Rewrite the sentences using the opposite of the adjective in bold. The meaning of the sentence should be the same.

1 Sandra is **quieter** than Julia.
Julia is louder than Sandra.

2 I find geography **easier** than science.
______

3 The ocean was **colder** than the swimming pool.
______

4 Juan's apartment is **smaller** than my house.
______

5 The weather in the spring is **cloudier** than in the summer.
______

6 Her second novel was **worse** than her first.
______

PRONUNCIATION
Weak forms: /ə/ in *than*

10.1 **Listen and complete the sentences with no more than two words.**

1 My new car is much ______ my last one.
2 This part of the city is ______ where I live.
3 Mount Everest is ______ Ben Nevis.
4 My father is four years ______ my mother.
5 The Nile is ______ the Amazon.
6 This shirt is more ______ the one online.

10.2 The Great Outdoors

VOCABULARY
Seasons and weather

Complete the words in the text. Use the first letter in bold to help you.

Japan: When to go and what to pack

[1]**S**__________ (March to May) is the best time of year to go as the weather is [2]**s**________ and you can see the amazing cherry blossom trees. It can still be a little [3]**w**________ so pack a sweater.

[4]**S**__________ (June to August) is fairly [5]**h**____, but it often [6]**r**________ in June. You should wear light clothes that dry quickly!

[7]**F**______ (September to November) can be [8]**f**________ especially in the hills. Remember to bring a jacket!

[9]In the **w**__________ (December to February) it [10]**s**________ a lot in the mountains and by the ocean and it can get very [11]**c**______. Wear boots and a scarf!

PRONUNCIATION
/oʊ/ and /aʊ/

Are the underlined sounds /aʊ/ or /əʊ/? Listen and circle the correct sounds.
10.2

1 cl<u>ou</u>dy /oʊ/ /aʊ/
2 c<u>oa</u>t /oʊ/ /aʊ/
3 m<u>ou</u>ntains /oʊ/ /aʊ/
4 l<u>ow</u> /oʊ/ /aʊ/
5 t<u>oe</u> /oʊ/ /aʊ/
6 <u>ou</u>tside /oʊ/ /aʊ/
7 n<u>ow</u> /oʊ/ /aʊ/
8 ph<u>o</u>ne /oʊ/ /aʊ/

GRAMMAR
Superlatives

A Complete the table.

Adjective	Comparative	Superlative
tall	taller	tallest
dry		
hot		
kind		
busy		
bad		
crowded		
ancient		
good		

B Use the prompts to write superlative sentences and questions.

1 Russia / big / country / in the world.
Russia is the biggest country in the world.

2 The Volga / long / river / Europe.

3 La Paz in Bolivia / high / capital city / world.

4 The mosquito / dangerous / insect / world.

5 Finland / happy / country / world.

6 What / fast / car / world?

7 What / wet / season?

8 Who / good / friend?

9 What / expensive / city / Europe?

10 Who / friendly / person you know?

VOCABULARY
Phrasal verbs

Complete the leaflet with the phrasal verbs in the box.

find out give up look for put on set off take off

1 Before you ________________, make sure you have everything you need.

2 ________________ information about where you are going and places along the way.

3 Pack things so they are easy to find; then you won't need to stop to ________________ them.

4 Wear a sweater and a coat. You can always ________________ one ________________ if you get hot.

5 If it gets really cold, ________________ a hat and scarf.

6 When you get tired, try not to ________________. It can be difficult to start again!

GRAMMAR
Verb + *to* + infinitive

A Reorder the words to make sentences. Add *to* in the right place.

1 get / married / in / June / hope / They
________________________________.

2 wanted / He / more / about / history / know
________________________________.

3 forget / Don't / Hannah / email
________________________________.

4 for / helping / me / keys / find / Thanks / my
________________________________.

5 Sam / college / trying / work / harder / is / at
________________________________.

B Are the sentences correct or incorrect? Correct the incorrect ones.

1 David never remembers locking the door – I'm surprised we haven't been robbed!
2 What have you decided doing?
3 Tina really needs to buy a new phone.
4 David plans visiting his cousin in Canada next year.
5 She learned reading when she was five years old.
6 I'm sorry, but I'd prefer to stay in a hotel.

PRONUNCIATION
Weak forms: /tuː/ and /tə/

10.3 Is *to* pronounced /tuː/ or /tə/ in these sentences? Listen and choose the correct sounds.

1 It's important to prepare before you set off. /tuː/ /tə/
2 Let's try to agree on a hostel. /tuː/ /tə/
3 Try to believe that you can do it. /tuː/ /tə/
4 Take some thick socks to put on when you get cold. /tuː/ /tə/
5 Be careful when you try to open your backpack. /tuː/ /tə/
6 Make sure you tell someone when you expect to arrive. /tuː/ /tə/

READING

A PREDICT Look at the pictures. What do you think the article is about?

B READ FOR GIST Read *For the fun of it* and check your ideas from Exercise A.

FOR THE FUN OF IT

LEO SAUNDERS | November 25, 2018 | 1289 COMMENTS

I love traveling – I even earn money writing about it for this magazine. I know most people say they enjoy traveling, but usually what they mean is spending time at their destination. For me it's getting there that is the most exciting part! I'm not interested in when, but how I get somewhere. My best trip this year was biking across the US along the most famous road in the world – Route 66. It's busy and dangerous, especially on a bike, but that's part of the fun. I could only travel about 80 miles a day, which wasn't a bad thing as it gave me time to look around and chat to some of the most interesting people I've ever met. Some of my new friends' stories were amazing. I went in September and I believe that is the best time to go if you're thinking about taking the same trip. It isn't too hot or cold along the route. The hottest part was in New Mexico where it was sunny every day. The whole trip took me just over a month to travel the 2400 miles from Los Angeles to Chicago, and it was amazing. Next year I plan to go along the Danube River in Europe by canoe!

Glossary

route (n) the road or path you use when you go from one place to another

C READ FOR DETAIL Read the article again and answer the questions.

1 Why does Leo think he's different from other travelers?
   - **a** He gets paid to write about traveling.
   - **b** He prefers the journey to the destination.
   - **c** He knows a lot of people who travel.

2 What doesn't interest Leo when he's traveling?
   - **a** Making new friends.
   - **b** Listening to people's stories.
   - **c** Getting somewhere quickly.

3 Why is it an advantage to travel slowly?
   - **a** It gives you time to see things.
   - **b** You don't worry about when you will arrive.
   - **c** You don't need to talk to people you meet.

4 What does Leo recommend his readers to do?
   - **a** Visit New Mexico.
   - **b** Try new experiences.
   - **c** Do the journey in September.

D IDENTIFY FACT AND OPINION Read the article again. Are these facts (F) or opinions (O)?

1 Most people enjoy traveling. ......
2 Leo is paid for writing about traveling. ......
3 Route 66 is in the US. ......
4 Biking on busy roads is often dangerous. ......
5 Leo biked about 80 miles a day. ......
6 September is the best time to travel along Route 66. ......
7 Route 66 is 2400 miles long. ......

E REFLECT Answer the questions.

1 Do you like traveling like Leo or is traveling just a way of getting somewhere?
2 What was the last journey you took? Where did you go? How did you travel?
3 Is there a place you would like to visit or travel to? Where is it? Why do you want to go there?

10.5 The Great Outdoors

LISTENING

10.4 **A LISTEN FOR GIST** Listen to a review. Which picture (1–2) matches the story?

1

2

Glossary

connect (v) to join two things together
remote (adj) not near a town or place where there are lots of people
spoiler (n) information about what happens in a story that you may not want to know about before reading a book, seeing a movie, etc for yourself

10.4 **B LISTEN FOR DETAIL** Listen again and check (✓) the topics that are discussed.

- **a** How they got to South America ☐
- **b** The location ☐
- **c** The weather ☐
- **d** What happened in the end ☐
- **e** When it happened ☐

10.4 **C LISTEN FOR SPECIFIC INFORMATION** Listen again. Complete the sentences with no more than three words from the review.

1. It is an ________ movie.
2. It is the ________ of what happened to two friends.
3. They were climbing in a ________ of the Andes.
4. They tried to climb faster because ________ was bad.
5. On the way down, Joel Sampson fell and ________.
6. There is a second ________ and Steven cuts the rope.
7. Joel Sampson survives and tries to get back to ________.
8. After ________, he reaches the camp and both men are alive.

D REFLECT Answer the questions.

1. What did you think of the story?
2. How do you think Joel Sampson survived?
3. Do you know any other stories of survival?

FUNCTIONAL LANGUAGE

Making and responding to invitations

10.5 Complete conversations (a–d) with the words and phrases in the box. Then listen and check.

come | free on | having | I'd love to | I'm away | sounds | to come | would be great

1

Vicky: Do you want to go and see that movie about the two mountaineers, Joel Sampson and Steven Gates, on Saturday? It's a true story and sounds amazing!

Sara: I'm sorry. [1] ________ this weekend.

2

Louise: Are you [2] ________ Thursday evening? We're going out to eat.

Dan: [3] ________, but I'm working.

3

Rob: We're [4] ________ a party tomorrow. Can you [5] ________?

Amy: Yes, that [6] ________ great.

4

Pavel: Would you like [7] ________ camping with me next month?

Mark: That [8] ________.

WRITING

A Label the picture with the items in the box.

a backpack   a camping stove   a first aid kit   a pair of walking boots

B Read the review page. Match reviews (a–c) with pictures (1–4). There is one extra picture.

C Complete the reviews with the adverb form of the adjectives in the box.

careful   easy   good   quick   ~~unfortunate~~

a I bought these to use when I go hiking. I had a pair, but they were very old. [1] *Unfortunately*, these ones don't keep your feet dry. They are also difficult to put on. I need to buy a new pair that I can put on [2] ______.

b I got this for when I go camping. You need to use it [3] ______ and it works really [4] ______ for boiling water, but not for anything else. Next time I think I'll buy a more expensive model.

c My father bought this for me as a present. I had one before, but this one is bigger and lighter. It has lots of special parts so I can find things [5] ______. I love it.

D Read the reviews again. Write notes about each using the table below.

	Review a	Review b	Review c
What is the product?			
What are its bad points?			
What are its good points?			
Would the reviewer recommend it?			

WRITING PRACTICE

A PREPARE You are going to write a review for a product you recently bought. Use the questions in Exercise D to help you write notes.

B WRITE Use your notes and some adverbs to write your review. Remember to use adverbs of manner.

VOCABULARY
The body

Label body parts (1–10) with the words in the box.

arm brain ear eye foot hand heart leg neck nose

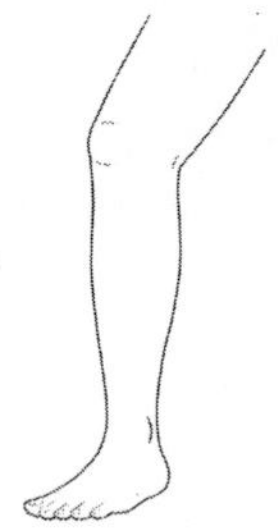

1 ....

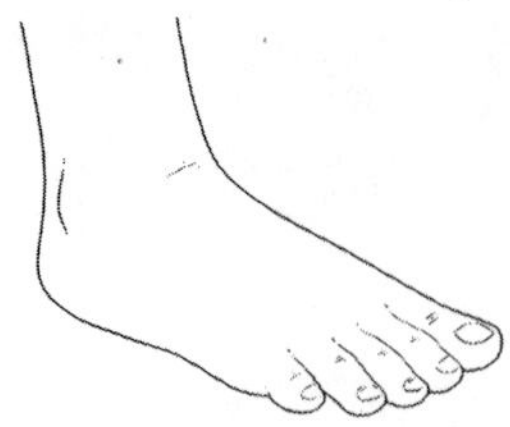

2 ....

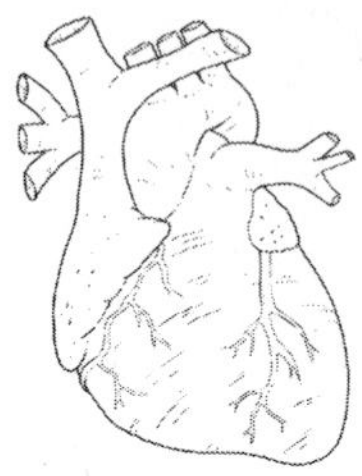

3 ....

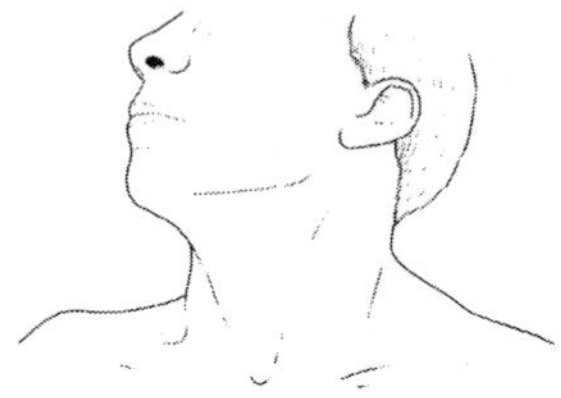

4 ....

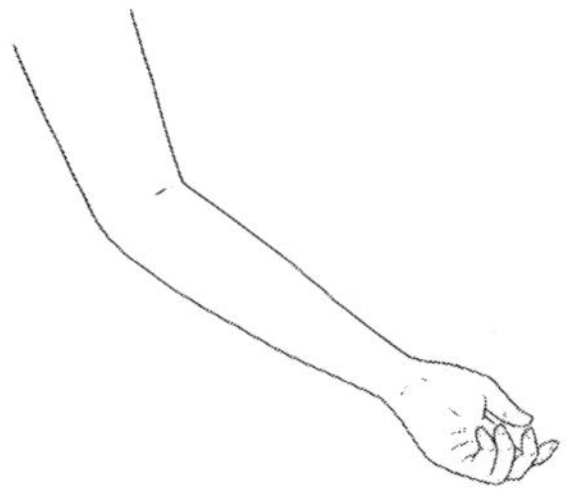

5 ....

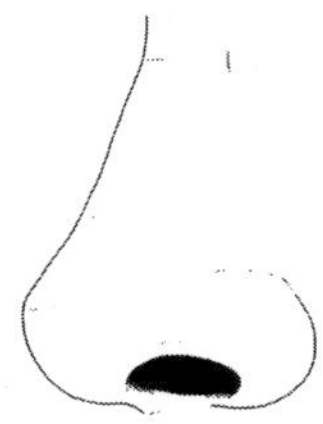

6 ....

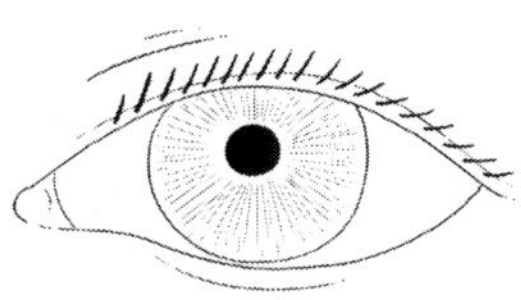

7 ....

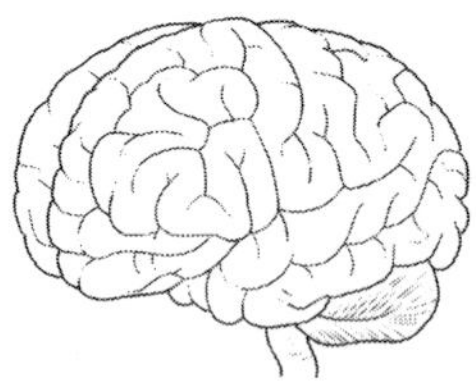

8 ....

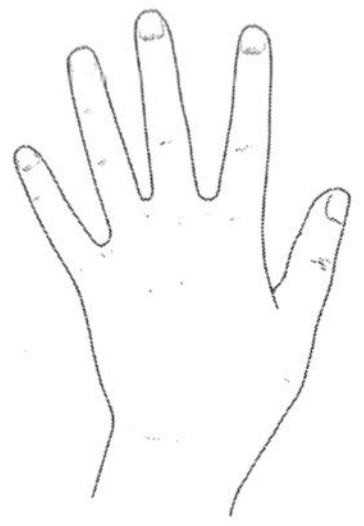

9 ....

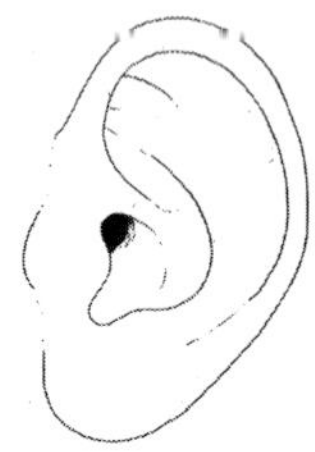

10 ....

GRAMMAR
should and *shouldn't*

A Correct the mistakes in each sentence.

1 We should go to the beach today or tomorrow?
2 A: I should buy John a birthday present.
B: No, you should. He didn't buy you one.
3 We're going on vacation in August so the weather should sunny.
4 They shouldn't to talk to their mom like that.

B Give advice using *should* or *shouldn't* for the following situations.

1 Rachel always feels tired in the morning. (*don't go to bed late*)
You shouldn't go to bed late.
2 Lucy always feels sick after eating nuts. (*don't eat nuts*)
You ....
3 Brad hasn't studied for his exam next week. (*study now*)
You ....
4 Your friend works too hard. (*relax more*)
You ....
5 Your friend always drives everywhere he goes. (*walk sometimes*)
You ....

PRONUNCIATION
Sentence stress

11.1 **Listen and repeat the sentences. Underline *should* or *shouldn't* if it is stressed.**

1 You should try to eat lots of fruits and vegetables.
2 You shouldn't drink too much tea.
3 You should get plenty of exercise.
4 You shouldn't worry about it too much.
5 You should exercise your brain every day.

GRAMMAR
Present perfect

A Use the prompts to write present perfect sentences or questions.

1 you / meet / famous person?
Have you ever met a famous person?

2 you / ride / elephant?
____

3 I / not go / Japan
____

4 she / write / ten books
____

5 I / not live / abroad
____

6 you / run / marathon?
____

B Look at Roberto's and Lucy's Bucket Lists (the things they want to do before they die). Complete the sentences using the present perfect.

Lucy's Bucket List	Roberto's Bucket List
swim with dolphins [✓]	buy a house [✗]
climb Kilimanjaro [✗]	go to New York [✓]
eat octopus [✓]	eat octopus [✓]
fly a plane [✓]	take a photo on the Great Wall of China [✗]
win the lottery [✗]	win the lottery [✗]

1 Lucy *has swum* with dolphins.
2 Roberto ______________ a house.
3 Lucy ______________ Kilimanjaro.
4 Roberto ______________ to New York.
5 They ______________ octopus.
6 Lucy ______________ a plane.
7 Roberto ______________ on the Great Wall of China.
8 They ______________ the lottery.

VOCABULARY
Irregular past participles

Choose the correct past participles (a, b or c) to complete the sentences.

1 Ben's not here today. He's … on vacation.
a been **b** gone **c** taken

2 Libby's favorite soccer team haven't … a game this year.
a finished **b** done **c** won

3 I've never … a camel before. This will be the first time.
a gone **b** ridden **c** taken

4 Greg is very careless. He's … his leg again!
a broken **b** done **c** eaten

5 I've … too much. I have a stomach ache.
a done **b** eaten **c** seen

6 Come on! I'm sure you've … enough photos.
a had **b** done **c** taken

7 Oh no! I've … to bring any money! Can you pay for me?
a forgotten **b** remembered **c** had

8 Don't worry. I've never … any sharks here and I come to this beach every year.
a ridden **b** eaten **c** seen

PRONUNCIATION
Past participles

11.2 Listen and circle the past participle that has a different sound.

1	done	forgotten	run
2	eaten	forgotten	won
3	gone	ridden	taken
4	been	ridden	seen
5	won	broken	eaten

GRAMMAR
Present perfect vs simple past

A **Choose the correct options to complete the sentences.**

1 ***I've played / I played*** soccer with some of my friends from work last night.

2 It says here that ***he joined / he's joined*** the company five years ago.

3 ***We went / We've been*** to an amazing Japanese restaurant for dinner on the weekend.

4 I went to Barcelona last year, but I ***never went / 've never been*** to Madrid.

5 The weather was terrible yesterday. It ***'s rained / rained*** all day.

6 I love running marathons. I ***did / 've done*** three already this year.

B **Complete the sentences with the present perfect or simple past form of the verbs in parentheses.**

1 I ______________ (*go*) to Istanbul for a conference last week.

2 He ______________ (*climb*) two mountains this year.

3 *The Secret History* is my favorite book. I ______________ (*read*) it seven times!

4 We ______________ (*see*) an amazing movie at the movie theater last night!

5 My parents ______________ (*get married*) ten years ago.

6 I ______________ (*not see*) the news today. What's happening?

PRONUNCIATION
Contractions

11.3 **Listen and check (✓) the sentences you hear. Then listen again and repeat the sentences.**

1 ☐ **a** He has been climbing for ten years.
☐ **b** He's been climbing for ten years.

2 ☐ **a** He has never been afraid of heights.
☐ **b** He's never been afraid of heights.

3 ☐ **a** You have always been adventurous.
☐ **b** You've always been adventurous.

4 ☐ **a** I have never had an accident.
☐ **b** I've never had an accident.

5 ☐ **a** I've always enjoyed rock climbing.
☐ **b** I have always enjoyed rock climbing.

VOCABULARY
Sports

Label pictures (1–10) with *go*, *do* or *play* and a sport.

1 ______________

2 ______________

3 ______________

4 ______________

5 ______________

6 ______________

7 ______________

8 ______________

9 ______________

10 ______________

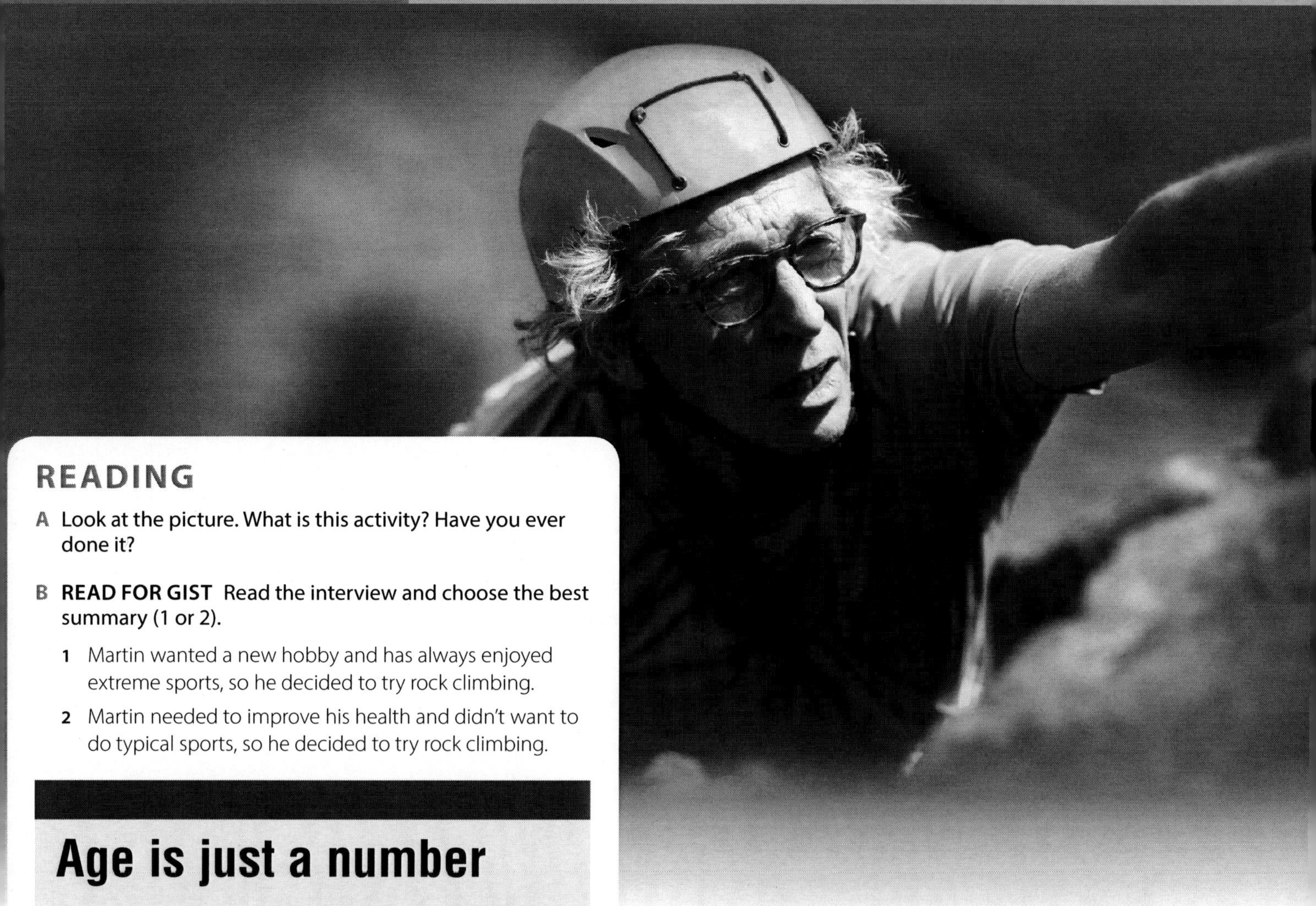

READING

A Look at the picture. What is this activity? Have you ever done it?

B **READ FOR GIST** Read the interview and choose the best summary (1 or 2).

1 Martin wanted a new hobby and has always enjoyed extreme sports, so he decided to try rock climbing.
2 Martin needed to improve his health and didn't want to do typical sports, so he decided to try rock climbing.

Age is just a number

Do you want to do something more exciting? This week, we're talking to Martin Lutt, a rock climber, who is 74!

So when did you start rock climbing?

I've been a climber for about ten years. The first time I tried it was on my birthday. My doctor told me to do more exercise, but I didn't want to play golf or go to the gym so I decided to do something more adventurous.

It's fairly dangerous, were you not worried?

No, not really. I've never been afraid of heights and I have always enjoyed exciting sports, so rock climbing seemed like a good idea. I joined a local club and learned to climb on an indoor wall. I did my first outdoor climb two years ago. It was such a great experience. I've done six more since then, and I still practice on the indoor wall every week.

Have you ever injured yourself?

Yes, I broke a bone in my foot last year. It took a long time to get better, but now I can climb again and I'm planning my next adventure!

Glossary

adventurous (adj) new, unusual and exciting
injure (v) hurt or cause pain

C **READ FOR DETAIL** Read the interview again. Are these sentences true (T) or false (F)? Correct the false sentences.

1 Martin has been a rock climber all his life. T / F
2 His wife told him to do more exercise. T / F
3 He wasn't interested in playing golf or going to the gym. T / F
4 He isn't afraid of heights. T / F
5 He wants to continue climbing. T / F

D **IDENTIFY THE SEQUENCE OF PAST EVENTS** Read again. Number the events in the order they happened.

...... Martin broke a bone in his foot.
...... The doctor told Martin to do more exercise.
...... Martin did his first outdoor climb.
...... Martin learned to climb on an indoor wall.
...... Martin joined a local club.

E **REFLECT** Answer the questions.

1 Is rock climbing popular in your country?
2 Which new sport would you like to try?
3 Do you prefer team or individual sports? Why?

11.5 The Body

Listening; Functional Language

LISTENING

11.4 **A LISTEN FOR KEY WORDS** Listen to a conversation about exercise. Check (✓) the sports that are discussed.

11.4 **B LISTEN FOR DETAIL** Listen again. Choose the correct names to complete the sentences.

1 *Sophie / Hannah* feels tired.
2 *Sophie / Hannah* often goes for a run when she feels tired.
3 *Sophie / Hannah* goes to a yoga class.
4 *Sophie / Hannah* has tried yoga and didn't like it.
5 *Sophie / Hannah* decides to go to a boxing class.
6 *Sophie / Hannah* says it's a good way to protect herself.

C REFLECT Answer the questions.

1 Do you do any of the sports that Sophie and Hannah talk about?
2 What do you think of the different sports?
3 Would you like to join a boxing class? Why/Why not?

FUNCTIONAL LANGUAGE

Asking for information

A Complete the conversation with the words in the box.

are there	can I	do I	how long	how much	when

Receptionist: Good afternoon, can I help you?
Sophie: Yes, I'd like some information about your boxing classes.
Receptionist: OK, great. What would you like to know?
Sophie: [1] ______ are the classes?
Receptionist: They're on Tuesdays and Fridays at seven o'clock in the evening.
Sophie: Twice a week … great. And [2] ______ are the classes?
Receptionist: They finish at nine o'clock. So they're two hours.
Sophie: Perfect. That's not too late. [3] ______ do they cost?
Receptionist: It's $8 per class or $35 for five classes.
Sophie: Hmm … I think I'll go for five classes. [4] ______ need to bring any equipment?
Receptionist: No, just your usual gym clothes. We provide gloves …
Sophie: Great! [5] ______ any lockers for our bags?
Receptionist: Yes, they're in the changing rooms. Just bring a lock.
Sophie: OK, I have one at home. [6] ______ pay for the classes now?
Receptionist: Yes, of course. Please can I have your card number?

11.5 **B** Listen and check your answers to Exercise A.

WRITING

A Read the post on a health website. What's it about?

My doctor says I need to lose some weight and try to live a healthy lifestyle. The problem is I don't like sports, I prefer watching TV. I know one thing I should do is eat healthy food, but I love cakes and chocolate too much and I don't want to give them up. Does anyone have any advice?

Larry March 7, 3:10 pm

B Read the three recommendations (1–3). Which do you think is the best one? Why?

1 Hi Larry, I feel your pain. When I get home from work, I'm tired [1]____________ and don't want to do anything. I turn on the TV, get some food from the kitchen and hardly move for the rest of the evening. Don't worry about your weight, as long as you feel happy.

Jasmine March 8, 7:57 pm

2 Larry, your doctor's right. Exercise is very important for you. Why don't you try something like swimming? It's good for you and it's relaxing. It's nice as you can do it on your own, but you do need to find a swimming pool that isn't too far away. You could walk to the swimming pool – that would [2]____________ help.

Sammy March 8, 11:09 pm

3 Hi there, I understand you don't like sports, but there are simple things you can do like walk or bike everywhere. Of course, you'd need to buy a bike if you don't already have one. Your diet is important; try to eat healthy food and limit yourself to one piece of chocolate a week [3]____________.

Trevor March 11, 7:15 am

C Read the recommendations again. Answer these questions.

1 What advice does Jasmine give?

2 What sport does Sammy suggest?

3 What two pieces of advice does Trevor give?

D Complete the recommendations with the adverbs in the box.

also	as well	too

WRITING PRACTICE

A PREPARE You are going to write a recommendation for Larry. Write notes. Think about why your advice would be good for Larry and what problems there might be.

B WRITE Use your notes to write a recommendation for the forum. Use *also, too* and *as well* to add information.

GRAMMAR
going to

A **Use the prompts and *going to* to complete the sentences and questions. Use contractions where possible.**

1 you / do / tonight / ?
What are you going to do tonight?

2 I / go / the movie theater / with my friends

3 Tim / not finish / his essay

4 How / you / get home / ?

5 Emma / start college / in September

6 My mother / not cook / tonight

7 What / you / have / for lunch / ?

8 Darren / run / a marathon / this weekend

B **Look at Sophie's weekly planner and complete the short text with *going to* or *not going to*.**

Mon:	*meet Joe for lunch*	✓
Tues:	*go to the dentist's*	✗
Wed:	*visit Mom in the hospital*	✓
Thurs:	*play tennis with Beth and Amanda*	✓
Fri:	*buy a new pair of shoes*	✗
Sat:	*take the children to the park*	✓
Sun:	*watch Matthew play soccer*	✗

Sophie has a busy life. Here is a typical week of hers. On Monday she's [1] ________ meet Joe for lunch and then go shopping. On Tuesday she has an appointment at the dentist's, but she's [2] ________ go because she hates the dentist. On Wednesday she's [3] ________ visit her mother in hospital. Then on Thursday she's [4] ________ play tennis with her friends. On Friday she was planning to go shopping to buy new shoes, but now she's [5] ________ go because she doesn't have enough money. On Saturday she's [6] ________ take the children to the park, but on Sunday Sophie is [7] ________ watch Matthew play soccer because she's [8] ________ stay at home and relax.

PRONUNCIATION
going to: weak and strong *to*

12.1 **Read the sentences and circle /tə/ or /tuː/. Then listen, check and repeat.**

1 Are you going to watch TV tonight? /tə/ /tuː/
2 How are you going to eat all of that? /tə/ /tuː/
3 Sophie is going to meet Joe for lunch. /tə/ /tuː/
4 I'm not going to ask you again! /tə/ /tuː/
5 Sophie isn't going to buy a new pair of shoes. /tə/ /tuː/

VOCABULARY
Future time expressions

Correct the mistakes in these sentences.

1 Do you know what time we're going to arrive next tomorrow?
2 Simon's going to travel to New York on weekend.
3 I'm going to call Giovanni and ask him to soon come over.
4 Are you going to study at the university year next?
5 Megan is going to get married this one summer.
6 They're not going to arrive here until later this tonight.

GRAMMAR
will for predictions

Read the email from Susie. Complete Amy's reply with *will* and *won't*.

To: Amy.Chen@inbox.org
From: Susie21@media.co.uk
Subject: News!

Hi Amy, I'm really excited as I'm moving to Shanghai next week to start a new job. In fact, it's my first job because I've just graduated from the university where I studied Art and Design. My job is to teach English to young children in a school. I've never taught English before, but I like children. I don't speak Chinese, but I'm going to take lessons. I'm not very good at learning languages and I hope Chinese isn't too difficult. My biggest worry is that I'm vegetarian, I don't eat meat and I'm not very good at cooking. I hope there are good places to eat.

Love, Susie

To: Susie21@media.co.uk
From: Amy.Chen@inbox.org
Subject: Re: News!

Hi Susie, it's great to hear from you. I'm sure you 1 ________ love Shanghai. It's a nice city and you 2 ________ find a lot to do there. Here's a photo of my brother and his friends. He went there on vacation last year. I know you 3 ________ find life there very different and you 4 ________ be able to sleep in late. It's going to be very different from when you were a student! I'm sure you 5 ________ enjoy the job as well. As for learning Chinese, you 6 ________ find it easy, Chinese is a very difficult language, but I know you 7 ________ try your best. What about the food? You 8 ________ definitely find it difficult as a vegetarian, but there are a lot of new restaurants opening so you 9 ________ have a problem finding a few places to eat. Maybe you 10 ________ learn to cook. ☺

Love, Amy

VOCABULARY
Collocations with *get*

Complete the conversations with the phrases in the box.

get a coffee | get any sugar | get home | get some cash | getting married | get some new clothes | got a new job

Sara: Hi Jane! It's good to see you again. Do you want to 1 ________?

Jane: That's a great idea, but I'll need to go and 2 ________ out.

Sara: Don't worry! I'll pay for it. I just 3 ________.

Jane: Oh, really? Wow! So we have a lot to talk about then!

Sara: Here's your coffee. I didn't 4 ________ …

Jane: Oh, that's fine, I don't take sugar. So, when do you start your new job?

Sara: Next month. I need to 5 ________; everyone dresses so well in that office! What about you? Any news?

Jane: Haven't you heard? Steve and I are 6 ________ …

Sara: Oh wow! That's wonderful news.

Jane: Thanks! Oh! Look at the time …

Sara: What's wrong?

Jane: Nothing, but I promised Steve I'd 7 ________ by four o'clock.

Sara: OK. Well it was nice to see you again. Bye.

PRONUNCIATION
Contractions: *'ll*

12.2 Listen and check (✓) the sentences you hear. Then listen again and repeat the sentences.

1 ☐ **a** You will love it there.
☐ **b** You'll love it there.

2 ☐ **a** I'm sure you will enjoy the job.
☐ **b** I'm sure you'll enjoy the job.

3 ☐ **a** Susie will find Chinese difficult.
☐ **b** Susie'll find Chinese difficult.

4 ☐ **a** We will be able to speak Chinese together.
☐ **b** We'll be able to speak Chinese together.

5 ☐ **a** You will find plenty of places to eat.
☐ **b** You'll find plenty of places to eat.

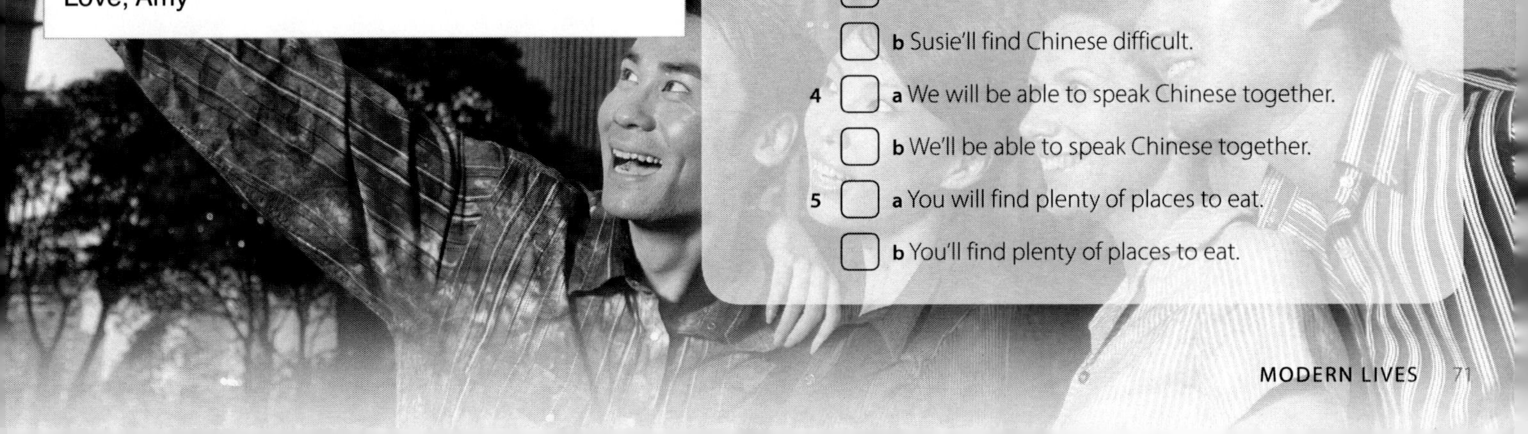

VOCABULARY
Internet communication

Complete the text with the words in the box.

blog chat connected follow likes share tweet uploaded

My name is Charlie Reid and I'm a professional photographer. I have a travel ¹__________ where I write about my adventures and ²__________ my photos. Here's one I ³__________ last week when I was in Antarctica. I can see how many people ⁴__________ me and one thing that's very interesting is to see the number of ⁵__________ my photos get. It's amazing how easy it is to stay ⁶__________ to people around the world. In fact, I use social media to ⁷__________ with my daughter when I'm away from home. I don't ⁸__________ yet, but I guess I should.

PRONUNCIATION
Diphthongs

12.3 **A Match the words with the same underlined sound. Then listen and check.**

1	Facebook	a	post
2	used	b	now
3	like	c	boot
4	choose	d	enjoy
5	mouse	e	eight
6	follow	f	cute
7	point	g	try

12.4 **B Listen and circle the word with a different diphthong in each group.**

1	menu	chat	human
2	video	follow	tourist
3	blog	noise	boy
4	mouth	now	know

GRAMMAR
might

A Complete the conversation with *might* or *might not* and a verb in the box.

be go join leave see stay take

Phil: Hi Lucy. It's Phil.
Lucy: Hi Phil. Where are you?
Phil: I'm on my way, but I ¹__________ a little late. I have to finish this report at work.
Lucy: Oh, OK. How long do you think you'll be?
Phil: I'm not sure. It ²__________ another half an hour or so. Why?
Lucy: Well, we ³__________ here much longer. We thought we ⁴__________ soon.
Phil: Really? Where will you go?
Lucy: I'm not too sure. The others are talking about going to another place, but I ⁵__________ them, I ⁶__________ home instead.
Phil: Right, well I'll be as quick as I can and I ⁷__________ you there.
Lucy: OK, I'll text you if we leave.
Phil: Thanks.

B Choose the correct responses (a or b) to the questions.

1 Have you decided what you're doing next year?
   a Yes, I have a job at my dad's company, so I'm going to work there.
   b Yes, I have a job at my dad's company, so I might work there.
2 Do you have any plans for the weekend?
   a I'm not sure. I'm going to meet some friends and go shopping.
   b I'm not sure. I might meet some friends and go shopping.
3 What do you think you'll be doing in ten years' time?
   a That's a difficult question. I'm going to move to Australia.
   b That's a difficult question. I might move to Australia.
4 Are you going on vacation this year?
   a I'm not sure yet. I might go to Spain with some friends in the summer.
   b I'm not sure yet. I'm going to Spain with some friends in the summer.

12.4 Modern Lives

Reading

READING

A PREDICT Look at the title of the blog post and the picture. What do you think the post is about?

B SCAN Read the blog post quickly to check your ideas from Exercise A.

C READ FOR GIST Read the blog post and check (✓) the topics that Mike makes predictions about.

- ☐ cell phones
- ☐ photos
- ☐ power
- ☐ battery
- ☐ robots
- ☐ houses
- ☐ education
- ☐ internet

Calling home

by Mike Samuelson

People often ask me what the next new thing is going to be in the world of communication. I always say that making predictions is not easy, but then I guess as a technology expert it is my job. I now have about 100,000 people who read my blog posts every week and about 3 million followers on Twitter. It always amazes me how many people seem to be interested in what I have to say.

Fifteen years ago most people only used their cell phones to make a phone call, but today we use them to take photos, send messages, go on the internet, pay for things in stores ... and we don't make many phone calls! In the next five years the power of our cell phones will increase even more. One thing that might change a lot is the battery. In the future we might have phones that use water for power. I also think we'll use our phones to connect with the things we have at home. So we'll turn the lights on before we get home. We'll send a message to our fridge and we'll have a robot that takes our food out and puts it in the microwave to cook. Next week I'm going to blog about the future of transportation ...

Glossary

communication (n) talking or writing to give or exchange information

expert (n) someone who has a special skill or knows a lot about something

power (n) the energy that makes something work

D READ FOR DETAIL Read the blog again. Choose the correct options (a, b or c) to complete the sentences.

1 Mike is always surprised at how ...
   - a easy it is to make predictions.
   - b many people follow him on Twitter.
   - c many people are interested in his opinions.

2 Mike ...
   - a has 100,000 followers on Twitter.
   - b writes a blog about technology.
   - c works for a technology company.

3 Mike says that 15 years ago ...
   - a the most common use for a cell phone was to call someone.
   - b most people didn't have a cell phone.
   - c people used their cell phones to do lots of things.

4 Mike says that today people don't often use their cell phones to ...
   - a pay for things in stores.
   - b make calls.
   - c connect to the internet.

5 Mike predicts that in the future we'll use cell phones ...
   - a only when we're at home.
   - b to cook our food.
   - c that use energy from water.

E REFLECT Answer the questions.

1 What do you use your cell phone for most?

2 Has the way you use your phone changed? If yes, how?

3 Do you use social media like Twitter and Facebook? How?

12.5 Modern Lives

Listening; Functional Language

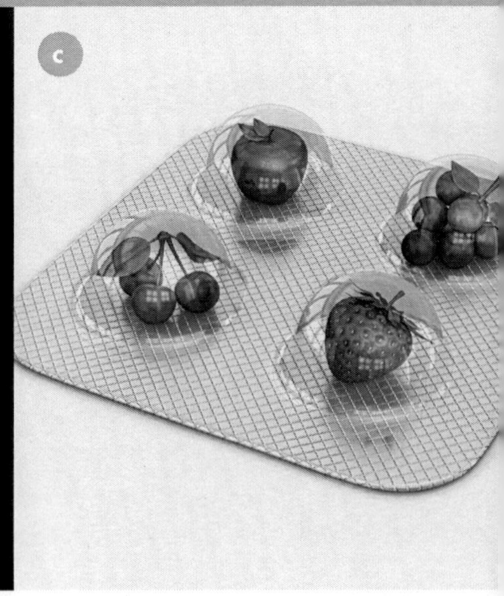

LISTENING

A PREPARE You're going to listen to a podcast about the future. Look at pictures (a–c). What do you think the speakers might talk about?

12.5 **B LISTEN FOR GIST** Listen to the podcast. Match speakers (1–3) to pictures (a–c). How many of your predictions in Exercise A did you get right?

Glossary

podcast (n) a radio show you can download and play on a computer, phone or tablet
prediction (n) what you think will happen in the future

12.5 **C LISTEN FOR DETAIL** Listen again. Are these sentences true (T) or false (F)? Correct the false sentences.

1 Tom thinks everyone will drive the same cars as today. *T / F*
2 He doesn't think we will have jetpacks. *T / F*
3 When Jenny was young, she had a cell phone. *T / F*
4 Jenny thinks we'll have robots doing most of the work. *T / F*
5 Richard doesn't think life will change. *T / F*
6 Ellen likes the idea of eating food that isn't fresh. *T / F*

D REFLECT Answer the questions.

1 Do you agree with any of the people? Which one(s)?
2 What are your predictions for the future?

FUNCTIONAL LANGUAGE
Showing interest in something

12.6 Complete the conversation with the expressions in the box. Then listen and check.

don't worry	I love it	it doesn't matter
no problem	that's a shame	that's terrible

Laura: Hi Ellen, I'm sorry I'm late!
Ellen: 1 ______________.
Laura: I was going to text, but I realized I'd left my phone at home.
Ellen: 2 ______________. I just did some shopping.
Laura: I'm always too busy to go shopping. Did you buy anything?
Ellen: Yes, I bought this dress. What do you think?
Laura: 3 ______________! You'll look amazing in it.
Ellen: Thanks. So do you want to go and get a coffee?
Laura: Sure. Oh no! I've lost my wallet.
Ellen: What? 4 ______________!
Laura: I'm sorry, but I can't go for a coffee now.
Ellen: 5 ______________, but I understand.
Laura: I'm going to see if I left it on the bus.
Ellen: 6 ______________! The most important thing is to find your wallet. Call me later.
Laura: OK, I will. Bye!

12.6 Modern Lives

June 2nd – A day for our son! Hosted by Angus and Julia The Baytree York, UK.

Come and join us to celebrate our son's graduation. Liam's graduation ceremony will be at 10 am on June 2nd. We are planning a small party for friends and family after the graduation ceremony finishes. We've booked a private room at The Baytree in York and there will be food and drink for 50 guests.

Please send replies to Lara Stevenson as she is organizing everything for us.

WRITING

A Read the invitation. What's it for?

a an anniversary
b a birthday
c a graduation
d a wedding

B Put these sentences and phrases in the correct order to make a reply.

☐ Also, we will rent a car at the airport. Is there a parking lot at The Baytree where we can leave the car?

☐ Can you let us know if there are any rooms at The Baytree, or can you suggest a suitable hotel?

☐ Dear Ms. Stevenson,

☐ I am writing to you to inform you that we plan to attend Liam's graduation party on June 2nd.

☐ Kind regards, Pierre (and Mari) Lefevre

☐ We look forward to hearing from you.

☐ We will fly over from France on June 1st, so we will need to stay at a hotel in York.

C Read the reply again. Answer these questions.

1. Why are they writing to Ms. Stevenson?
2. Where are the Lefevres traveling from?
3. When will they arrive in the UK?
4. How are they going to travel from the airport?
5. What do they want to know about The Baytree?

WRITING PRACTICE

A Read the invitation. What's it for?

Amy's 21

March 28th – 21!
Hosted by Ed and Mary

Come and join us to celebrate Amy's 21st! Yes, our daughter is 21. It's amazing how quickly they grow up! We have hired a party organizer for this special occasion, so please contact them for any information you might need. We hope to see you all there.

Contact PartyTime at: partytime@mail.com

B **PREPARE** You are going to write an email asking for information. Think about what you need to know. Write notes.

C **WRITE** Use your notes to write your formal email.

Irregular Verbs

Base form	Simple past	Past participle
be	was/were	been
become	became	become
begin	began	begun
break	broke	broken
bring	brought	brought
build	built	built
buy	bought	bought
can	could	(been able to)
catch	caught	caught
choose	chose	chosen
come	came	come
cost	cost	cost
cut	cut	cut
do	did	done
drink	drank	drunk
eat	ate	eaten
fall	fell	fallen
feel	felt	felt
find	found	found
forget	forgot	forgotten
get	got	got
give	gave	given
go	went	gone/been
grow	grew	grown
have	had	had
hear	heard	heard
hit	hit	hit
hold	held	held
hurt	hurt	hurt
keep	kept	kept
know	knew	known
leave	left	left
lend	lent	lent
let	let	let
lose	lost	lost
make	made	made
mean	meant	meant
meet	met	met
must	had to	(had to)
pay	paid	paid
put	put	put
read	read	read
ride	rode	ridden
run	ran	run
say	said	said
see	saw	seen
sell	sold	sold
set	set	set
shut	shut	shut
sing	sang	sung
sit	sat	sat
sleep	slept	slept
speak	spoke	spoken
spell	spelled	spelled
spend	spent	spent
stand	stood	stood
steal	stole	stolen
take	took	taken
teach	taught	taught
tell	told	told
think	thought	thought
throw	threw	thrown
understand	understood	understood
wear	wore	worn
win	won	won
write	wrote	written

PHONETIC SYMBOLS											
Single vowels			Diphthongs			Consonants					
/ɪ/	fish	/fɪʃ/	/uw/	new	/nuw/	/p/	pen	/pen/	/s/	snake	/sneɪk/
/iː/	bean	/biːn/	/eɪ/	face	/feɪs/	/b/	bag	/bæg/	/z/	zoo	/zuː/
/ʊ/	foot	/fʊt/	/ɔɪ/	boy	/bɔɪ/	/t/	tea	/tiː/	/ʃ/	shop	/ʃɒp/
/uː/	shoe	/ʃuː/	/oʊ/	nose	/noʊz/	/d/	dog	/dɒg/	/ʒ/	television	/'telɪvɪʒən/
/e/	egg	/eg/	/ju/	use	/juz/	/ʧ/	chip	/ʧɪp/	/m/	map	/mæp/
/ə/	mother	/'mʌðər/	/aɪ/	eye	/aɪ/	/ʤ/	jazz	/ʤæz/	/n/	name	/neɪm/
/ɜː/	word	/wɜːrd/	/aʊ/	mouth	/maʊθ/	/k/	cake	/keɪk/	/ŋ/	ring	/rɪŋ/
/ɔː/	talk	/tɔːk/				/g/	girl	/gɜːrl/	/h/	house	/haʊs/
/æ/	back	/bæk/				/f/	film	/fɪlm/	/l/	leg	/leg/
/ʌ/	bus	/bʌs/				/v/	verb	/vɜːrb/	/r/	road	/roʊd/
/ɑː/	arm	/ɑːrm/				/θ/	thing	/θɪŋ/	/w/	want	/wɔnt/
/ɒ/	top	/tɒp/				/ð/	these	/ðiːz/	/j/	yes	/jes/

UNIT 7

Lesson 7.5, Listening, Exercise A

4 **P = Presenter T = Tom**

P: Joining us now to talk about his latest TV show is the British explorer, Tom Kingsley. Tom, welcome to the show.

T: Thanks for having me.

P: So, Tom – in the show you attempt to travel around the world without flying. Can you tell us a little about your experience?

T: Sure. So I left London and went by train to Paris. From there I took a bus that went through six countries in Europe before I arrived in Athens, Greece. Next, I went by boat to Egypt. After arriving and doing some sightseeing, I rented a car and I drove all the way to Kenya, though I had to go by ferry to cross into Sudan. In Nairobi I found a ship that could take me to India. In Mumbai I bought a motorcycle and rode from India, across South-East Asia all the way to Singapore. I spent a month there before I found another boat that could take me all the way to the US. It took three weeks to arrive! Finally, I took the bus and train across the US.

P: Wow! That sounds like an amazing journey.

T: It really was. It was pretty difficult at times, but I met a lot of amazing people and stayed in some very unusual places.

P: I'm sure you did. Were there any surprises?

T: Well, to be honest, the most difficult part was checking into my first hotel in the US. After traveling so far and staying in so many unusual places, it was kind of strange to be somewhere so normal again!

Lesson 7.5, Functional Language

.5 **R = Receptionist T = Tom**

R: Good afternoon, sir. How can I help you?

T: I have a reservation for a double room for two nights.

R: OK, great. Could I have your passport, please?

T: Of course. Here you are. What time is checkout on Sunday?

R: It's at noon, sir.

T: Great, and is breakfast included?

R: Yes, it is. It's between 6:30 and 10 am in the dining room. Do you need any help with your bags?

T: No, I'm fine thank you. Is there wi-fi in the rooms?

R: Yes, there is. The password is on the desk in your room.

T: OK, great. Thank you.

R: You're welcome, sir. Do you need anything else?

T: Uh . . . yes. Can I have my key?

UNIT 8

Lesson 8.5, Listening, Exercise A

.4 **O = Oli T = Tara**

O: So what's your favorite food, Tara? Sushi? Pasta?

T: Actually, I love American food.

O: Really! What? Like hot dogs and burgers?

T: Mmmm . . . yes, they're delicious, especially when you cook them on a barbecue!

O: Yes, but that kind of food is so unhealthy!

T: I know, I know . . . but I don't eat it very often. Actually, during the week, I usually eat something simple like salad, or pasta. Anyway, what about you? What's your favorite food?

O: Uh, it's difficult to choose, but Thai food is probably my favorite.

T: Oh, really? Isn't it really hot and spicy?

O: Uh, a lot of the dishes are, yes. But my favorite is made with coconut milk, so it isn't spicy at all. I usually make it with noodles and lots of vegetables . . .

T: No, stop – you're making me hungry!

O: Ha ha! Sorry. Should we go and get some lunch?

T: Yes, please. I'm starving! Why don't we go and have some Italian food?

O: But I thought you like American food?

T: I do, but there's a really good pizza place near here. The slices are enormous!

O: Sounds great, let's go!

Lesson 8.5, Functional Language, Exercise B

8.5 **W = Waiter T = Tara**

W: Are you ready to order?

T: Yes, I'll have the chicken salad, please.

W: OK. Would you like something to drink?

T: Could I have a mango juice with ice?

W: Certainly.

W: Would you like to see the dessert menu?

T: No, thanks. Can I have the bill, please?

UNIT 9

Lesson 9.5, Listening, Exercise A

9.4

1 We are a new store opening soon in the shopping center. We offer designer brands at low prices. Max Out is perfect for all those people looking for a bargain.

2 JCs – the local family store with really friendly staff. Come in and talk to us and we'll help you find what you are looking for. There are lots of new items each week, so why not visit and see what we have in stock?

3 Why wait for the sales? At Bargains 2day we have something for everyone. The price is low, but the quality is high.

4 Looking for something special to wear on the weekend? At Tuffin, we only sell quality clothing. Yes, our prices are expensive, but we believe you get what you pay for.

5 TieUp is a great place to shop for all those little things. We sell ties, scarves, gloves and sunglasses at a discount. For all those small things in your wardrobe, TieUp is the place to look.

Lesson 9.5, Functional Language
9.5 **S = Store clerk C = Customer**

S: Good morning. Can I help you?

C: No, I'm just looking, thank you. Oh! Actually, can I try these jeans on, please?

S: Of course, the changing rooms are over there.

S: Oh! They look really great on you . . .

C: Thank you, but I think they are a little small. Do you have the same style in medium?

S: Yeah, here you are.

C: These are perfect. How much are they?

S: They're $35, but there's a 10% discount.

C: Oh, great! I'll take them.

UNIT 10

Lesson 10.5, Listening, Exercise A
10.4 YouTuber: Hello YouTube, and welcome to another episode of *Lost the plot*. Each week I tell you the plot of a new movie in just one minute. Oh, and remember, there will be spoilers! This week I'm talking about Wes Carpenter's new adventure movie *A Long Way Down*.

It tells the true story of two friends, Joel Sampson and Steven Gates, who try to climb to the top of a mountain in a remote part of the Andes in South America. The two friends reach the top of the mountain, but on their way down, the weather becomes really bad and they try to climb faster. Unfortunately, Joel falls on the way down and breaks his leg. The two friends carry on trying to get to the bottom of the mountain, but the situation gets worse. Then another accident happens and, in the end, Steven cuts the rope that connects the two men together. Joel falls again, but somehow he survives. When he finds out he is alone on the mountain, he tries to get back to their camp. It takes him three days, but finally he makes it. Amazingly, the two men both live to tell the story.

Lesson 10.5, Functional Language
10.5 **V = Vicky S = Sara L = Louise D = Dan R = Rob A = Amy P = Pavel M = Mark**

1

V: Do you want to go and see that movie about the two mountaineers, Joel Sampson and Steven Gates, on Saturday? It's a true story and sounds amazing!

S: I'm sorry. I'm away this weekend.

2

L: Are you free on Thursday evening? We're going out for a meal.

D: I'd love to, but I'm working.

3

R: We're having a party tomorrow. Can you come?

A: Yes, that sounds great.

4

P: Would you like to come camping with me next month?

M: That would be great.

UNIT 11

Lesson 11.5, Listening, Exercise A
11.4 **S = Sophie H = Hannah**

S: I feel so tired.

H: What you need is exercise, Sophie.

S: Exercise? How will that make me less tired?

H: You'd be surprised. When I feel tired, I go for a swim or a run and I always feel better afterward.

S: Hmm . . . I might have to give it a try.

H: You could come with me when I go to my next yoga class.

S: No, thanks. I've tried yoga and I didn't enjoy it.

H: Well, there are lots of other sports you could do. Let me show you the local health club's website. Hmm . . . Here you go.

S: Oh, look. They have boxing classes.

H: Boxing! Are you crazy?

S: No, why shouldn't I learn to box?

H: Well, I guess you'll get fit . . .

S: Yes, and learn to protect myself.

H: Let me know how it goes. I might join you at the classes.

Lesson 11.5, Functional Language, Exercise B
11.5 **R = Receptionist S = Sophie**

R: Good afternoon, can I help you?

S: Yes, I'd like some information about your boxing classes.

R: OK, great! What would you like to know?

S: When are the classes?

R: They're on Tuesdays and Fridays at seven o'clock in the evening.

S: Twice a week . . . great and how long are the classes?

R: They finish at nine o'clock. So they're two hours.

S: Perfect. That's not too late. How much do they cost?

R: It's $8 per class or $35 for five classes.

S: Hmm . . . I think I'll go for five classes. Do I need to bring any equipment?

R: No, just your usual gym clothes. We provide gloves.

S: Great! Are there any lockers for our bags?

R: Yes, they're in the changing rooms. Just bring a lock.

S: OK, I have one at home. Can I pay for the classes now?

R: Yes, of course. Please can I have your card number?

UNIT 12

Lesson 12.5, Listening, Exercise B

.5 **E = Ellen T = Tom J = Jenny R = Richard**

1

E: Hello and welcome to The Lowdown. I'm your host Ellen Michaels and on today's show we're talking to people on the street about their predictions for the future. Hi, what's your name?

T: Hi I'm Tom! I'm 22 and I'm a student.

E: So Tom, how do you think life will change in the next 20 years?

T: Wow! That's a big question. Well, I don't think we'll be driving around in cars . . .

E: Ha ha ha. Do you think we'll have jetpacks?

T: Um, no. I think we'll have flying cars.

2

E: Excuse me, can I ask you a few questions?

J: Sure.

E: So, first of all. What's your name and how old are you?

J: I'm Jenny and I'm 56.

E: So you must have seen a lot of changes over the years. How do you think life will change in the next 20 years?

J: That's a difficult question. When I was young, there were no cell phones and look at today. I think one change is that we'll have robots doing most of the jobs.

3

R: Hi, I'm Richard and I'm a retired firefighter from New York.

E: How do you think life will change over the next 20 years?

R: Well, I don't really know to be honest . . . Maybe we'll all eat food that comes in packages . . .

E: You mean we won't have fresh food?

R: Yes, exactly. I know it's a shame, but I think that's what will happen.

E: Yuck!

Lesson 12.5, Functional Language

2.6 **L = Laura E = Ellen**

L: Hi Ellen, I'm sorry I'm late!

E: Don't worry!

L: I was going to text, but I realized I'd left my phone at home.

E: It doesn't matter. I just did some shopping.

L: I'm always too busy to go shopping. Did you buy anything?

E: Yes, I bought this dress. What do you think?

L: I love it! You'll look amazing in it.

E: Thanks. So do you want to go and get a coffee?

L: Sure. Oh no! I've lost my wallet.

E: What? That's terrible!

L: I'm sorry, but I can't go for a coffee now.

E: That's a shame, but I understand.

L: I'm going to see if I left it on the bus.

E: No problem! The most important thing is to find your wallet. Call me later.

L: OK, I will. Bye!

Answer key

7.1 Getting around

VOCABULARY

A

1 subway train **2** taxi **3** ferry **4** plane **5** trolley
6 bicycle

B

1 boat **2** plane **3** bicycle **4** trolley **5** bus **6** motorcycle

PRONUNCIATION

/eɪ/	/oʊ/
main	boat
plane	coach
same	motorcycle
train	phone

GRAMMAR

1 could **2** couldn't **3** couldn't **4** could **5** could
6 couldn't

7.2 A love of adventure

VOCABULARY

A

1 travel **2** the flight **3** the scooter **4** the hotel
5 the motorcycle

B

1 returned from New York
2 take a taxi
3 arrived at the hotel
4 missed the bus
5 left the station

GRAMMAR

2 Mae didn't study German at school.
3 I didn't see Simon and Alison at the party on Saturday.
4 I didn't go to the gym after work.
5 I didn't like math when I was in school.
6 Lizzie didn't finish the report yesterday.
7 I didn't speak to him after the meeting.
8 Molly didn't enjoy that movie last night.

PRONUNCIATION

2 Bangkok **3** Berlin **4** Caracas **5** Milan **6** Kathmandu
7 Lisbon **8** Manila **9** Mumbai **10** Chicago

7.3 A trip to remember

GRAMMAR

2 Did you go **3** where did you have **4** what did you eat
5 was **6** Did you take **7** When did

PRONUNCIATION

1 What did‿you‿do on the weekend?
2 How long did‿you work there?
3 They stayed there for‿two weeks.
4 Susan didn't want‿to‿go home.
5 Did‿you have fun?
6 Where did‿you‿go last summer?
7 Did‿you stay‿in‿a hotel?
8 We went to‿a lot‿of museums.

VOCABULARY

1 went **2** got **3** met **4** ate **5** took

7.4 Reading

READING

A

1 c **2** a **3** b

B

1 a **2** b **3** b **4** a **5** a **6** a **7** b **8** a

C

1 farm worker **2** hostel worker **3** tour guide **4** tour guide
5 hostel worker **6** farm worker **7** farm worker

7.5 Listening; Functional Language

LISTENING

A

B

1 T
2 F (He traveled from Paris to Athens by bus.)
3 F (He bought a motorcycle in Mumbai.)
4 T
5 F (He says he met a lot of amazing people.)
6 T

FUNCTIONAL LANGUAGE

1 afternoon **2** reservation **3** passport **4** checkout
5 included **6** help **7** wi-fi **8** password

7.6 Write a short article about a travel experience

WRITING

A

1 c **2** a **3** e **4** d

B

1 December or Cambodia **2** expensive hotel
3 souvenirs **4** too hot **5** tourists

C

1 because **2** so **3** because **4** because **5** so

WRITING PRACTICE

B

Model answer

A few years ago, I went to Shanghai in China with my two friends. We all love modern cities, so we were excited to go.
Shanghai is a huge city with lots of restaurants, stores and hotels. We stayed at a hotel in Jing'an – an area of the city famous for its large temple. It wasn't too expensive and the rooms were very clean.
There are two sides of the city to visit – Puxi, which is more historical, and Pudong, which is famous for its skyscrapers. We did a lot of sightseeing and shopping in both sides of the city!
For me it was a wonderful trip because it was so different from where I am from. Also the food was delicious. I would definitely recommend going.

8.1 I'm hungry!

VOCABULARY

A

Down

2 rice **5** fish **7** milk **8** orange

Across

3 yogurt **4** coffee **6** tomato **9** banana **10** juice

GRAMMAR

A

This week, I'm trying to be healthier. So instead of snacks like a bar of chocolate, I'll eat ~~any~~ **some** fruit, like ~~a~~ **an** apple, a banana or some oranges. I never eat breakfast, but this morning, I had a bowl of cereal with milk~~s~~ and a toast without ~~some~~ **any** butter.
At lunchtime, I went to a café near where I work. I ordered some brown rice~~s~~ with chicken and a glass of juice~~s~~. Then for dessert I had some yogurt.
In the evening, I usually have some sandwiches, but this evening, I'm going to have some fish~~es~~ with ~~a~~ vegetables and ~~any~~ **some** cheese~~s~~ and biscuits.

B

Countable singular	Countable plural	Uncountable
apple	chips	pasta
banana	hamburgers	rice
cookie	potatoes	toast
mushroom	sandwiches	yogurt

PRONUNCIATION

1 chips **2** tomatoes **3** peas

8.2 What we eat

VOCABULARY

1 rice **2** sparkling water **3** yogurt **4** chocolates **5** sauce
6 yogurt

PRONUNCIATION

Short vowel sounds: apple, bread, chicken, eggs, cup
Long vowel sounds: beans, cheese, food, fruit, tea

GRAMMAR

A

1 much **2** a lot of **3** many **4** a lot of **5** much
6 a lot of **7** a lot of **8** many **9** much **10** much

B

1 How ~~many~~ **much** bread do you usually eat?
2 correct
3 Karen drinks ~~much~~ **a lot of** coffee in the morning.
4 correct
5 There aren't ~~much~~ **many** bananas left. Can you buy some?
6 How ~~much~~ **many** people did you invite to the party?

8.3 Yes, chef!

GRAMMAR

A

1 a or an **2** the **3** no article **4** the **5** no article

B

1 – **2** an **3** – **4** the **5** – **6** the **7** an **8** an **9** a
10 the **11** the **12** The **13** a **14** the

PRONUNCIATION

1 flour **2** fruit **3** healthy **4** bottle **5** vegetables
6 fry **7** bowl **8** sandwich

VOCABULARY

A

1 Put **2** Crack **3** Beat **4** Heat **5** fry **6** Serve

B

1 peel **2** grate **3** Put **4** serve **5** fry **6** chop **7** Add

8.4 Reading

READING

A

2 Unusual food

B

1 c **2** a **3** b **4** c **5** b

C

1 adjective **2** noun **3** verb **4** adjective **5** noun

D

1 c **2** d **3** a **4** e **5** b

8.5 Listening; Functional Language

LISTENING

A

1 Oli **2** Tara **3** Tara

B

1 c **2** b **3** b **4** b **5** a **6** c

FUNCTIONAL LANGUAGE

A

1 f **2** d **3** b **4** a **5** c **6** e

8.6 Write an online restaurant review

WRITING

A

2 one of the cats
3 the waitress
4 the chocolate cake and tea with milk
5 the café

B

1 it **2** It **3** It **4** she **5** they **6** them **7** she **8** him

C

1 His girlfriend
2 The restaurant was dark. / They couldn't see the menu.
3 Pasta
4 Delicious
5 It was cold.

WRITING PRACTICE

B

Model answer

Carlo's ★★★★☆

I love Italian food, so I was really pleased when this restaurant opened in the city center. I went there for my birthday last month with a group of friends and family. The restaurant has huge wood-burning ovens and you can see the chefs making the pizza. There are over 30 different types of pizza to choose from. The waiter was from Naples and was very helpful. He told us which pizzas were his favorite so we ordered those!

9.1 People watching

VOCABULARY

1 cap, jeans, sneakers
2 skirt, scarf, coat, boots, socks
3 boots, jeans, sweater
4 sunglasses, jeans

PRONUNCIATION

1 skirt **2** prefer **3** nurse **4** earn **5** work **6** girl
7 person **8** learn

GRAMMAR

A

2 'm looking **3** you're shopping **4** Sara is helping
5 Are we / having **6** I'm / We're leaving **7** Is Ben coming
8 is he working **9** he isn't working

B

1 Is he riding a bike? **2** Is he eating pizza?
3 Is she playing the piano? **4** Are they running in the park?

C

1 Yes, he is. **2** Yes, he is. **3** Yes, she is. **4** No, they aren't.

9.2 Job swap

VOCABULARY

A

1 These days **2** at the moment **3** today **4** right now
5 now **6** currently

B

1 currently **2** right now **3** today **4** now **5** these days
6 At the moment

GRAMMAR

A

1 work **2** isn't helping **3** are they watching **4** ride
5 walks **6** are you leaving **7** aren't closing

B

1 You should wear a scarf – **it's snowing** outside.
2 We ~~aren't~~ **don't** usually play~~ing~~ tennis every day.
3 correct
4 **Do** ~~Are~~ you usually go~~ing~~ to the beach?
5 correct
6 She isn't currently cook**ing** in the kitchen.
7 Are they walk**ing** to school?

PRONUNCIATION

1 sung **2** walking **4** pink **5** younger **8** strong

9.3 Shop till you drop

GRAMMAR

A

Subject pronoun	Object pronoun
I	me
he	him
she	her
it	it
we	us
you	you
they	them

B

1 us **2** it **3** them **4** it **5** him **6** her **7** you

VOCABULARY

A

1 dentist's **2** pharmacy **3** bank **4** department store
5 hairdresser's

B

2 bakery **3** butcher's **4** market **5** bookstore **6** library
7 newsstand **8** department store

PRONUNCIATION

1 /tʃ/ **2** /ʃ/ **3** /ʃ/ **4** /tʃ/ **5** /ʃ/ **6** /ʃ/ **7** /tʃ/ **8** /ʃ/

9.4 Reading

READING

A

1 b **2** a

B

1 be easy **2** for a walk **3** much fun **4** really sleep
5 to walk everywhere **6** enough time **7** in the end

C

1 damage **2** organizing **3** uploading **4** crazy
5 under pressure **6** terrible

9.5 Listening; Functional Language

LISTENING

A

b 5 **c** 4 **d** 3 **e** 2

B

1 T
2 F (Max Out has lots of bargains.)
3 T
4 F (They sell high-quality products at low prices.)
5 T
6 F (You can buy ties, scarves, gloves and sunglasses at TieUp.)

FUNCTIONAL LANGUAGE

1 Can I help you **2** I'm just looking **3** can I try
4 the changing rooms **5** look really great **6** a little small
7 in medium **8** How much are they **9** I'll take them

9.6 Write a social media post

WRITING

A

2

B

1 Mae **2** Hannah **3** Luke **4** Hannah **5** Luke **6** Hannah

C

1 We're **going** for our usual walk through the woods.
2 You have to be careful as some are ~~in danger~~ **dangerous,** but there are lots that are delicious.
3 We're having a ~~grate~~ **great** time and trying to see how high we can get.
4 ~~I am~~ **I'm/I am** happy we're inside~~.~~**, as** ~~As~~ we don't have to worry about the weather.
5 We're traveling down to London to watch a play~~?~~**.**
6 ~~m~~**M**om packed some sandwiches for us~~.~~ so we're all eating those.

WRITING PRACTICE

B

Model answer

We're at the beach for the first time this year. We're all so happy! Sophie's going to go for a swim; Juan and Luca are playing volleyball. As for me, I'm relaxing and sunbathing for the rest of the day! Tom.

10.1 The right location

VOCABULARY

A

1 lake **2** island **3** forest **4** mountains **5** beaches
6 ocean **7** hills **8** jungle **9** river **10** desert

GRAMMAR

A

2 older
3 easier
4 more famous
5 better
6 cheaper
7 closer
8 more expensive
9 dirtier
10 worse
11 more comfortable
12 stranger

B

2 I find science harder / more difficult than geography.
3 The swimming pool was hotter / warmer than the ocean.
4 My house is bigger / larger than Juan's apartment.
5 The weather in the summer is sunnier than in the spring.
6 Her first novel was better than her second.

PRONUNCIATION

1 bigger than **2** busier than **3** higher than
4 younger than **5** longer than **6** expensive than

10.2 Where on Earth?

VOCABULARY

1 Spring
2 sunny
3 windy
4 Summer
5 hot
6 rains
7 Fall
8 foggy
9 winter
10 snows
11 cold

PRONUNCIATION

1 /aʊ/ **2** /oʊ/ **3** /aʊ/ **4** /oʊ/
5 /oʊ/ **6** /aʊ/ **7** /aʊ/ **8** /oʊ/

GRAMMAR

A

Adjective	Comparative	Superlative
tall	taller	tallest
dry	drier	driest
hot	hotter	hottest
kind	kinder	kindest
busy	busier	busiest
bad	worse	worst
crowded	more crowded	most crowded
ancient	more ancient	most ancient
good	better	best

B

2 The Volga is the longest river in Europe.
3 La Paz in Bolivia is the highest capital city in the world.
4 The mosquito is the most dangerous insect in the world.
5 Finland is the happiest country in the world.
6 What is the fastest car in the world?
7 What is the wettest season?
8 Who is your best friend?
9 What is the most expensive city in Europe?
10 Who is the friendliest person you know?

10.3 Survival

VOCABULARY

1 set off **2** Find out **3** look for **4** take off **5** put on
6 give up

GRAMMAR

A

1 They hope to get married in June.
2 He wanted to know more about history.
3 Don't forget to email Hannah.
4 Thanks for helping me to find my keys.
5 Sam is trying to work harder at college.

B

1 David never remembers **to lock** ~~locking~~ the door – I'm surprised we haven't been robbed!
2 What have you decided **to do** ~~doing~~?
3 correct
4 David plans **to** visit~~ing~~ his cousin in Canada next year.
5 She learned **to** read~~ing~~ when she was five years old.
6 correct

PRONUNCIATION

1 /tə/ **2** /tuː/ **3** /tə/ **4** /tə/ **5** /tuː/ **6** /tuː/

10.4 Reading

READING

C

1 b **2** c **3** a **4** c

D

1 O **2** F **3** F **4** O **5** F **6** O **7** F

10.5 Listening; Functional Language

LISTENING

A

2

B

b, c, d

C

1 adventure **2** true story **3** remote part **4** the weather
5 broke his leg **6** accident **7** their camp **8** three days

FUNCTIONAL LANGUAGE

1 I'm away **2** free on **3** I'd love to **4** having **5** come
6 sounds **7** to come **8** would be great

10.6 Write a product review

WRITING

A

1 a camping stove **2** a backpack **3** a pair of walking boots
4 a first aid kit

B

a 3 **b** 1 **c** 2

C

2 easily **3** carefully **4** well **5** quickly

D

	Review a	Review b	Review c
What is the product?	A pair of walking boots	A camping stove	A backpack
What are its bad points?	They are difficult to put on and don't keep his feet dry	It can only really boil water	-
What are its good points?	-	It's good for boiling water	It's big and light It has lots of special parts
Would the reviewer recommend it?	No	No	Yes

WRITING PRACTICE

B

Model answer

I bought these gloves for my annual ski trip. They are made with a special material so you can grip the ski poles more easily. Unfortunately, they don't keep out the cold at all. I ended up having to buy a warmer pair at the ski resort.

11.1 Health tips

VOCABULARY

1 leg **2** foot **3** heart **4** neck **5** arm **6** nose **7** eye **8** brain **9** hand **10** ear

GRAMMAR

A

1 **Should we** ~~We should~~ go to the beach today or tomorrow?
2 A: I should buy John a birthday present.
B: No, you should**n't**. He didn't buy you one.
3 We're going on vacation in August so the weather should **be** sunny.
4 They shouldn't ~~to~~ talk to their mom like that.

B

2 You shouldn't eat nuts.
3 You should study now.
4 You should relax more.
5 You should walk sometimes.

PRONUNCIATION

1 You should try to eat lots of fruits and vegetables.
2 You shouldn't drink too much tea.
3 You should get plenty of exercise.
4 You shouldn't worry about it too much.
5 You should exercise your brain every day.

11.2 In it to win it

GRAMMAR

A

2 Have you ever ridden an elephant?
3 I've never been to Japan. / I haven't been to Japan.
4 She's written ten books.
5 I've never lived abroad. / I haven't lived abroad.
6 Have you ever run a marathon?

B

2 Roberto hasn't bought a house.
3 Lucy hasn't climbed Kilimanjaro.
4 Roberto has been to New York.
5 They have (both) eaten octopus.
6 Lucy has flown a plane.
7 Roberto hasn't taken a photo on the Great Wall of China.
8 They haven't won the lottery.

VOCABULARY

1 b **2** c **3** b **4** a **5** b **6** c **7** a **8** c

PRONUNCIATION

1 forgotten **2** won **3** gone **4** seen **5** won

11.3 Move it

GRAMMAR

A

1 I played **2** he joined **3** We went **4** 've never been
5 rained **6** 've done

B

1 went **2** has climbed / 's climbed **3** have read / 've read
4 saw **5** got married **6** haven't seen

PRONUNCIATION

1 b
2 a
3 b
4 b
5 a

VOCABULARY

1 play golf
2 play badminton
3 go swimming
4 do gymnastics
5 play tennis
6 do yoga
7 play basketball
8 go surfing
9 do karate
10 go ice-skating

11.4 Reading

READING

B

2

C

1 F (He started ten years ago.)
2 F (His doctor told him to do more exercise.)
3 T
4 T
5 T

D

1 The doctor told Martin to do more exercise.
2 Martin joined a local club.
3 Martin learned to climb on an indoor wall.
4 Martin did his first outdoor club.
5 Martin broke a bone in his foot.

11.5 Listening; Functional Language

LISTENING

A

boxing, running, swimming, yoga

B

1 Sophie **2** Hannah **3** Hannah **4** Sophie
5 Sophie **6** Sophie

FUNCTIONAL LANGUAGE

A

1 When
2 how long
3 How much
4 Do I
5 Are there
6 Can I

11.6 Write a recommendation on a forum

WRITING

A

Losing weight

C

1 Not to worry about his weight
2 Swimming
3 Walk or bike everywhere, try to eat healthy food and not so much chocolate

D

1 too / as well **2** also **3** too / as well

WRITING PRACTICE

B

Model answer

Hi Larry, why don't you try watching aerobic videos online? There are some really good ones for people who are starting to exercise more. It also means you can exercise at home. You could try eating more fruit as well.

12.1 Life's too busy

GRAMMAR

A

2 I'm going to go to the movie theater with my friends.
3 Tim isn't going to finish his essay.
4 How are you going to get home?
5 Emma is going to start college in September.
6 My mother isn't going to cook tonight.
7 What are you going to have for lunch?
8 Darren is going to run a marathon this weekend.

B

1 going to **2** not going to **3** going to **4** going to
5 not going to **6** going to **7** not going to **8** going to

PRONUNCIATION

1 /tə/ **2** /tuː/ **3** /tə/ **4** /tuː/ **5** /tə/

VOCABULARY

1 Do you know what time we're going to arrive ~~next~~ tomorrow?
2 Simon's going to travel to New York on **the** weekend.
3 I'm going to call Giovanni and ask him to ~~soon~~ come over **soon**.
4 Are you going to study at the university **next** year ~~next~~?
5 Megan is going to get married this ~~one~~ summer.
6 They're not going to arrive here until later ~~this~~ tonight.

12.2 Everything will be shiny

GRAMMAR

1 will **2** will **3** will **4** won't **5** will **6** won't **7** will
8 will **9** won't **10** will

VOCABULARY

1 get a coffee **2** get some cash **3** got a new job
4 get any sugar **5** get some new clothes **6** getting married
7 get home

PRONUNCIATION

1 b **2** a **3** a **4** b **5** b

12.3 Communication

VOCABULARY

1 blog **2** share **3** uploaded **4** follow **5** likes
6 connected **7** chat **8** tweet

PRONUNCIATION

A

2 f
3 g
4 c
5 b
6 a
7 d

B

1 chat **2** tourist **3** blog **4** know

GRAMMAR

A

1 might be **2** might take **3** might not stay **4** might leave
5 might not join **6** might go **7** might see

B

1 a **2** b **3** b **4** a

12.4 Reading

READING

C

cell phones, power, battery, robots

D

1 c **2** b **3** a **4** b **5** c

12.5 Listening; Functional Language

LISTENING

B

1 b
2 a
3 c

C

1 F (He thinks there will be flying cars.)
2 T
3 F (When Jenny was young there were no cell phones.)
4 T
5 F (Richard doesn't think life will be the same as it is now.)
6 F (Ellen hates the idea of not eating fresh food.)

FUNCTIONAL LANGUAGE

1 Don't worry
2 It doesn't matter
3 I love it
4 That's terrible
5 That's a shame
6 No problem

12.6 Write a formal email

WRITING

A

c

B

1 Dear Ms. Stevenson,
2 I am writing to you to inform you that we plan to attend Liam's graduation party on June 2nd.
3 We will fly over from France on June 1st, so we will need to stay at a hotel in York.
4 Can you let us know if there are any rooms at The Baytree, or can you suggest a suitable hotel?
5 Also, we will rent a car at the airport. Is there a parking lot at The Baytree where we can leave the car?
6 We look forward to hearing from you.
7 Kind regards, Pierre (and Mari) Lefevre

C

1 To say they will be coming and to ask for some information
2 France
3 June 1st
4 By car
5 If there are any rooms available and if there is a parking lot

WRITING PRACTICE

A

A 21st birthday party

C

Model answer

Dear Sir/Madam,
I am writing to confirm I will be attending Amy's 21st birthday party on March 28th.
Can you please provide me with the address of the venue.
Also, what time does the party start and what time is it expected to end?
I look forward to hearing from you.
Kind regards,
Emma Sanchez

Notes

Notes

Notes